NEURO-QUEER

A Neurodivergent Guide to Love, Sex, and Everything in Between

By CJ DeBarra

2023

This trade paperback is published by Global Words Press.

This is a work of non-fiction. While all the events in this book are true, some names have been changed to protect the privacy of the people involved.

CATALOGING INFORMATION
ISBN: 978-1-911227-23-6
CREDITS
Editor: Victoria Villaseñor & Nicci Robinson
Cover Design: Nicci Robinson
Production Design: Global Wordsmiths

Acknowledgements

I have so many people to thank in the creation of this book, from friends to family to the wonderful people who gave up their time to be interviewed. Firstly, my partner, who, as well as the endless glasses of wine and support, gave me practical help with websites and design. I would have been lost without their technical support, good ideas, and the occasional reminder to eat dinner when my ADHD forgot.

Jennie Williams and Claire Holland from Enhance the UK, who not only gave me their time but also supported my voice as a neurodivergent person when not a lot of others did.

Victoria Villaseñor and Nicci Robinson at Global Wordsmiths, who answered an email from a frustrated and slightly drunk, fed-up writer. They got my voice and the idea of the book instantly, and it would not be here without their help and support. I cannot thank you enough.

Anastasia Galadza, Nora Nord, and Raven Faber took time out to speak with me from their schedules to be interviewed—at length…repeatedly.

The women, transgender, and non-binary folk who gave me their personal thoughts over email, phone, and Zoom. So many personal details and such openness was inspiring. I'm so grateful for your involvement, and I hope I've done your stories proud.

Finally, to S and R who are good, decent people whom I learned a lot from. Please don't sue me.

Dedication

To my family: Mum, Dad, Natalie, and the assorted cats and dogs. I love you all and please god may you all never read this book.

To my partner, who encouraged me to keep going with this and not put it in a drawer or set fire to it. This wouldn't have happened without you.
Love Giles X

This book is dedicated to all the ADHD women, transgender, and non-binary folk who have been told to stop daydreaming or sit still.

Chapter One
Growing up Rural

Neurotypical
Adjective: Not displaying or characterised by autistic or other neurologically atypical patterns of thought or behaviour.

Neurodiverse
Adjective: Displaying or characterised by autistic or other neurologically atypical patterns of thought or behaviour; not neurotypical.

If you're reading this book then you may have come for the whips, chains, and dildos as promised in the description. I'm hoping I can get you to stay for the love and relationships that accompanied that fun, as well as for a bit about what it means to be a fully fleshed neurodivergent human. Before we start talking about the messiness of sex however, I'm afraid you may have to get to know me first.

My personality, and who I perceive myself to be, has been affected by my ADHD. It's affected different areas of my life from the jobs I've had to the people I've dated. I'm a tall, green-haired, Gothy punk with the attention span of a goldfish. As an ADHD person, some of my experiences have been positive but others have been appallingly negative. A lot of this has had a direct impact on my relationships with others. I thought I would meet a man, fall in love, get married then have children and potentially a dog. But my ADHD, coming out as queer, and general *"not typical-ness"* has put paid to this resulting in me approaching middle-age and still being on Tinder.

But before I talk about the wonders of dating and relationships, I'm going to have to do some explaining as to how I ended up alone with just my cat for company. It's not that I'm complaining, but the cat is useless at conversation.

An Irish Childhood

It's hard to explain what growing up as gay and neurodivergent in rural Ireland was like. You had to be there…except not a lot of people were, resulting in a feeling of it being completely isolated. To some, the silence is comforting, and they find peace in the routines they develop but to others, like myself, this silence is deafening. The silence and the sheer lack of anything to do is the worst part of country life, especially for those of us who can't sit still or be quiet. There's nothing to pass the time other than sit and feel it passing you by minute by minute.

The small village I grew up in is on the coastline of Ireland, or as I often affectionately describe it, "the arse end of the country." My house was a short walk from a choice of different beaches, and you had to walk through thick woodlands to get there. West Cork is so beautiful that when you describe it to people, it sounds made up. Even my school overlooked the ocean. I was never far from the sea, something I now realise I took for granted as an adult stuck in the deep Midlands of England where I have to board a train for two hours to get to Skegness if I want a bit of beach life. Skegness just doesn't hit the same way if you've had beaches like I did.

I grew up on a steady diet of West Cork friendliness, culchie accents, and Catholicism. Not that I cared for any of it growing up. I was too busy being a teenager in the late '90s to notice the sea salt air or long sandy beaches near my home. I took for granted that these things would always be there. However, as time has moved on, new homes have been built, cliffs eroded, businesses opened. But while things have moved quickly on the surface, there's a lot that hasn't changed, like old attitudes. Below the surface, it's the same old Ireland masquerading as a new one.

But at that stage I was more interested in whatever nu-metal CDs I had bought, dying my hair strange colours, and trying to block out any romantic interest I had in girls. I stalked through the village in my boots to go sit and moodily write poetry with the usual embarrassing teenage flare for over-dramatising. Years later, I found that book of poetry and nearly died with mortification. I didn't just throw it in the bin, I tore up each page individually just in case anyone found it.

The village was tiny then. We had one small pub painted an intense yellow which stood out amongst the other white houses. The word BAR was confidently written across the top of the door in block letters. No fancy names here, just exactly what it was. It had an unofficial council of elderly men in the village who came twice a week for their Murphy's stout and discussion. The women weren't exactly unwelcome, but they certainly weren't encouraged to attend these discussions. Instead, they often sat at the end of the bar nursing half pints of lager while talking shop about the business of rural life. The village was almost a stereotype in how ridiculously Irish it was.

I avoided Mass and hanging out with other people. There were hardly any my age even if I did want to. The village did an excellent export in young people as they left in droves to go the cities for work or university. We all got out the second we could, which left the average age of the place at around fifty. Those of us who were *different* stayed away longer and chose not to return. If people did come back, it was often with kids or a partner to retire.

Those of us who had something different about us often visited but never stayed. After all, we'd made it out alive once, so who knew if we would manage to do so again. Being different meant the rural life would strangle us. Silence isn't for everyone.

We went to church on Sundays, confessions on Saturdays, were taught by nuns, and were surrounded by other Catholics. Northern Ireland was a foreign land a million miles away. We were too young to understand the troubles but would watch the conflict on TV as if it was happening in another country. We never met anyone who didn't go to Mass. The church was in every part of my growing up. I sang in the choir and was encouraged to sing solo, which I never wanted to do due to my nerves. The highest honour was bestowed on you as a child who volunteered for readings or choir solos, and if you did, the nuns left you alone.

I was baptised, then I did my first Holy Communion and my confirmation as a child. All of this was without any consent as I was so young. It was just expected that we would do these things without question. I wore the incredibly creepy white mini wedding dress like my friends and perched a small veil on my head like a child bride. They walked us up the aisle with boys from the nearby scoil bhuachaillí (boys' school). When Father Ryan asked what I wanted to be when I grew up, I said a nun, just like I'd been coached to say.

Even as a child, I knew I was different to my classmates, who seemed at ease with the nuns, the church, and our rural setting. I didn't always have the right words though, so the frustration erupted as a feeling of intense anger or bursts of energy.

My mother took me to a doctor when I was eleven. The letters from the doctor described ADHD perfectly.

"Her concentration is very poor, except for reading or artwork. She loves music and is always singing. Getting her to do something she doesn't want to do is extremely difficult. Her parents note that she runs clumsily, and her balance is not very good. She rushes and knocks things over. She is very impulsive, and her parents cannot trust her to cross the road. She could go out perfectly happily without socks or lunch."

Labelled

Reading those letters as an adult was extremely painful. I cried when they arrived, and I sat down to read them. ADHD was always framed so negatively when I was growing up that I developed a huge chip on my shoulder about it. I began to believe I was a fuck-up who wouldn't amount to anything.

ADHD felt like "the new thing now" in those

days. It had been imported from America where stories of over-medicated child zombies were filling the press. The media screamed about hyperactive children running riot until the super drug Ritalin got them to quieten down, but it robbed them of their personalities in the process. However, where I lived, this simply wasn't a thing, so there were no support systems in place for autistic or ADHD children. You either got the concept of schoolwork or you didn't. You were labelled the naughty child and put in your place as a troublemaker. You fell behind in your lessons while the other kids sailed ahead of you.

The only thing I remember from this time is the pressure placed on me to stay silent about what was happening. Mental health wasn't discussed. To this day, it still isn't talked about enough but it's better than it was. My mother was frantic that I should stay quiet and say nothing. "You don't want to be discussed," was her logic and I agreed, as it was better to not give the village any more gossip than you needed to.

There's a dreadful loneliness in silencing your struggle that Irish people do particularly well. Ask an Irish person how they are. Even if they have two broken legs and are on the floor writhing in agony, the answer will be, "Ah, yeah, grand, sure, you know yourself." Admitting to anything other than a headache when it comes to mental health is just not the done thing.

I felt resentful because my friends didn't seem to need pills to get on with their work, while I embarrassingly did. Yet somehow, I still didn't do my homework and felt like an outsider in class. The super pills didn't do what they were supposed to, much to my mother's disappointment, and it became evident the problems were still there in my friendships and schoolwork.

Eventually, Mam grew tired of me not doing my work. My father was around but in those days, looking after children and harassing them to do homework was *women's work*. My father left my mother to do it. She's still the emotional heavy-lifter in the house. She's the one I call about breakups or dead house plants. My father, a practical and lovely man, is the one I call to discuss house repairs or broken boilers. Mam took to calling the teachers to find out how much work I wasn't doing. Weeks of unfinished reports, maths, and essays were unearthed, and her rage was majestic.

I didn't hate school, but I just didn't understand why I didn't work like my classmates did. They found it so easy, whereas I struggled. Maths was my worst subject, but there was history and languages to contend with too. Cúpla focail? (Some words?) I was lucky if I managed aon focail (one word). There were a lot of glances and smirks when I was called on in class. "Miss Barra, cá bhfuil d'obair bhaile?" (Miss Barra, where is your homework?) would leave me in cold sweats. Why hadn't I learned it was easier to do the actual work?

I preferred to spend my time lost in a daydream, a book, or running around outside. I played long, elaborate childhood games that had everything from smugglers to ghost brides in them. I had a morbid interest in death and a fascination with the afterlife, so nearly all my games were slightly twisted. I would lose myself in the fantasy worlds I created for hours, barely coming up for food or to pee. I didn't want to break the magic of my imaginary universe by doing something that mundane.

When I discovered books, I began to write all of this down on paper. I thought I could create stories that people would read and maybe then they'd be able to see things as I did. I processed the world through these stories one creation at a time. I didn't realise that this creative imagination was a warning sign of two things: that I was potentially showing signs of inattentive, daydreamy ADHD and that I might end up a writer in later life. Only one of those things is treatable with medication. But for now, I was busy being the odd child out at school.

There was another reason for the exclusion I was feeling, but I hadn't figured it out yet. I started to feel an attraction to a girl in my class, which resulted in a lot of panic. I was about to go to the big school that had boys in it, so rather than panic about what it would be like to speak to a boy, like most of my classmates, I prayed these feelings would stop. There were no other queer people or any visibility on TV. I wasn't issued with a handbook on what it was or how to come out. Ireland only decriminalised homosexuality in 1993 when I was eight, not that we were aware of it. Divorce would follow in 1998 after a long, lengthy battle against the church.

When I got to secondary school, the differences that were accepted when we were younger became a cause for bullying not just by other children, but also by the nuns who taught us. The cruelty of these women was incredible and heightened by the fact that somehow, they were in the service of God. A short, thin nun called Sister Katherine told my mother, "There is nothing wrong with her. She just needs a good slap." That sums up the attitude towards neurodiversity in Ireland at that time. She said that I would amount to nothing and never go to college. I went on to get two degrees and a master's in journalism just to spite her.

I entered secondary school deeply insecure and with no confidence borne from years of being told how difficult I was. I was also struggling with subjects in school that I hadn't had to worry about before, like French. As a result, I started to be on my own at lunch—other kids didn't want to sit with me because I was different and acted strangely.

It hadn't been explained to me that regulating my emotions as an ADHD person is extra difficult. So I would form deeply emotional bonds with people only to have the friendships break down later. Regular teenage drama would be utterly heartbreaking and completely confusing for me.

I was always aware of the difference between me and the people in my class. I angrily decided this was down to ADHD. It started a long-standing hatred of having it mentioned or taken into account. I never told anyone I had it nor did I expect exceptions to be made when realistically I needed them.

I believed I was lucky that anyone even spoke to me. Looking back, it breaks my heart that I let people treat me that way. Accepting being shoved into doors. Told I was thick or stupid because my ADHD made answering out loud in class absolute hell. I kept my mouth shut, my head down, and I retreated into a world of make-believe when I had art class and at home. I would write stories before going to bed, when the cold fear of the next day would seep in.

The secondary school I attended was a stern building on the top of a hill overlooking the town.

Both the primary and secondary schools were in a small town, slightly bigger than my own village, which was surrounded by beaches and lagoons. PE meant walking around the lagoon a few times while the teachers counted down the minutes until the bell rang. The school gym, with its loose floorboards and birds nesting in it, was unusable. The school was attached to a functioning convent, which was the reason it had been built on the hill: to remind the town that the church was always there, always watching, and knew their every move. This meant that there were over a hundred steps to get to the front door, which nearly wiped us out every morning. We would push through the door on a cold morning, wheezing, sweating, and ready for the day.

The nuns floated around the school reminding us of their presence, statues glared down at us from every conceivable nook, and there were almost daily religious classes. The kids were imbued with this religious interference, and some teenagers blessed themselves as they drove past churches or if an ambulance screamed past. The kids also carried miraculous medal necklaces or rosary beads in pencil cases, and there were consequences to disobeying the religious ethos. Once, a girl in my class snuck out to an under-age disco and got caught. In response, her parents held her down on the table and hacked her hair off to the scalp with sharp scissors. She walked through the school with bald patches for weeks. What did we do when we saw this vicious child abuse? We turned our heads and ignored it. Literally pretended we couldn't see the cuts where the scissors had nicked her scalp.

In our final year, she approached me, her eyes

wide, and handed me a homemade leaflet.

"What's this?" I asked taking it from her.

"We're having a prayer circle at my house for all the women who have chosen to get abortions, so that they see the error of their ways," she said without a trace of emotion.

The nuns drilled into us that being different was shameful. That shame taught us to hide ourselves from each other. I never knew if anyone in my class was queer, autistic, or had any physical issues. We never knew if anyone had an abusive or broken home either. Divorce hadn't yet happened to Ireland, so many families stayed together during this time no matter how dangerous this could be (and often was) for those with abusive partners. Abortion was completely banned from even being discussed in public. "Never you mind about that. Nice girls don't need that," they said through pursed lips when we asked what it was in sex education. Years later, I watched friends, sisters, and colleagues silently travel to the UK for "the journey," which we never spoke about. Silence was learned young and taught well.

Secondary school was getting harder, with the lack of ADHD support affecting my schoolwork. I was nervous because of the bullying and anxious because I couldn't work at the speed the other children did. The subjects I enjoyed were English and Art, where I hid behind my creative streak. My worst subject was Irish.

ADHD makes you struggle to connect sequences quickly and off the top of your head. While other children rattled off, "An bhfuil cead agam dul go dtí an leithreas?" (Can I go to the toilet?), the teachers made me wait until I could say it before they'd let me go. Desperately needing to pee didn't help with trying to figure out how to ask for it in another language.

I had extra difficulties formulating a sentence because I couldn't figure out where a noun, verb, or adjective goes. French and Irish were so much of a nightmare for this reason that I just wouldn't speak. Mrs O' Donovan, my French teacher who had long since lost her patience with me, made several calls home about it. My mother took my case to the Department of Education to ask that I be exempt from languages as a direct result of my ADHD. While I was relieved, I was also embarrassed as it was another thing that marked me as different in the eyes of the other children in my class.

There was another problem as well. I had Oppositional Defiance Disorder (ODD), which is common in ADHD kids. It's defined as uncooperative, defiant, negative, irritable, and annoying behaviours towards parents, peers, teachers, and other authority figures. So I guess my neon green hair wasn't just about wanting to hide behind a layer of outlandishness. It was a form of saying "Fuck you" to the man. It worked. I was eventually expelled from school for "acting the maggot." In comparison to some of the horror stories of children getting expelled, my behaviour was nothing because I still had a healthy fear of consequences. But I definitely frustrated teachers. As the school became fed up with my uniform rule-bending, I stepped up my behaviour to include being a complete pain in the backside.

I became the teacher's worst nightmare: I cut holes in my uniform sleeves to stick my thumbs out of, I had multi-coloured hair, I drew metal band logos on every piece of homework, and I talked openly in class even after being asked to shut up. I once even asked a teacher if a lesbian kiss on a TV drama had turned her on, and I passed notes in every lesson.

I (along with others) eventually got expelled for screaming in class. We admitted to our screaming when questioned and were lined up downstairs to face the principal. Upon hearing I was expelled, I screamed "YES" loudly while raising a triumphant fist in the air. It had been weeks of no support from the school and getting detention for minor things like lack of participation in religious education. While I was so ready to leave, Mam was horrified by the phone call from the school to say I was being made to leave. Luckily, I was still able to sit my exams three weeks later. The school, not realising I studied incredibly hard in my spare time, were shocked when I came out with decent results. They had truly expected me to fail.

The Search for a Subculture

When I got older, I found my people. I discovered the Goths and my life changed. My dress sense went from "normal" to being covered in black, piercings, dyed hair, and coffin-shaped backpacks. It became my armour against the kids in my class who had been bullying me quite badly.

I applied a cheap white foundation all over my face and drew designs across my cheeks in heavy, black eyeliner. My poor mother, who had already been through a lot, despaired. "You're making a holy show of me," she exclaimed. During those years, she wouldn't be seen in town with me.

"Would you take off the white face paint at least?"
While my mother raised me listening to David
Bowie, Led Zeppelin, and Black Sabbath, she
somehow didn't expect me to take to it so well.
The black lipstick, blue hair, and piercings may have
been a little bit much for the parish in the early '00s.

That's something I've learned about ADHD later
in life. We have a tendency to lean into a new
hobby a little bit too hard. I wanted to hide behind
a facade of being different, because that's what was
expected from a girl who wore green mascara and
nose rings. No one would be shocked and more
importantly, the bullying might lessen a bit. My
outlandish outfits grew bolder, with knee-high stripy
socks, neon green hair, and pierced fingernails. That
last one horrifies me now as I recall driving thumb
tacks through my fingernails in science class before
bending rings to fit. How I didn't split my fingernails
in two is beyond me. I'd seen Janet Jackson in a
music video on MTV with rings in her nails, but it
never occurred to me that her nails were fake.

What my teachers didn't realise is that when my
ADHD combines with anxiety, as it often does, it
can make me painfully shy and afraid to speak. I
now realise my inability to speak in class was a panic
attack. When I wasn't helped or supported through
that panic attack, my ODD made me a nightmare to
deal with. As an adult, I dated a teacher who spoke
about kids in her school. She told me about them
setting fire to deodorant cans and bringing knives to
school. I can honestly say I was never that bad, but
those issues happen when kids aren't given enough
help or support.

Nowadays, there are support teachers, extra
classrooms, and teachers who are trained to spot

these sorts of things. Which is better than '90s rural Ireland was, but there's a long way to go, even now.

There are still children who fall through the cracks and leave with nothing because the schools are failing them. My friend M left school before the age of fifteen with no certificate because of undiagnosed autism, which he received no support with. He was diagnosed as an adult, and that explained a lot for him. His school days were a nightmare of bullying, isolation, and no support—all still crushingly common.

One of the greatest joys of ADHD is hyperfocus. I became locked into the idea of achieving an exceptional leaving certificate, so I knuckled down to study. I had correctly identified art college as the start of a new life where I could be myself. I studied obsessively morning to evening, barely coming up for food. My mother would contribute by buying me bottles of Lucozade so I didn't starve. I stayed in my room for hours, becoming irritated if I was dragged away from my books.

People often confuse ADHD with a lack of concentration, but it's really about how we can't regulate our attention like neurotypical people can.

Eat, sleep, study, Lucozade, repeat.

To this day I can't drink Lucozade.

I eventually passed my exams and got into the Limerick School of Art and Design (LSAD). That was my first time being around kids who were *all* the token weirdos of their schools. It was as if we were all rounded up and shipped off to one place. I found it incredibly overwhelming but, at the same time, welcome. After trying all the disciplines in the first year, at the last minute I decided to study sculpture instead of fashion design, which was why I'd chosen

LSAD.

It was easy to get distracted in college. Being in a university city equalled student nights every night of the week. Mondays always meant being turned out and up for Costello's, the local art college nightclub. Costello's was an old man's pub meets dive bar, with a carpet in the club area that was often soaked with drink about two songs into an evening. Ever the classy establishment, you could order a bag of cans to take away at the end of the night, and we loved it. It was home. Cheap naggins (small bottles of vodka) were bought and slipped in purses, joints were rolled and at the ready, then we were off. We would slide the owner a crisp, clean fiver before heading up the stairs into the darkened room. We shared a choice of nightclubs with other colleges during the rest of the week including University of Limerick (UL), Limerick Institute of Technology (LIT), and Mary Immaculate College (Mary I), which was where all the future teachers went and was nicknamed Mary Dry.

I was constantly distracted but in a fun way. I joined teams organising student events, and I started volunteering to raise money for HIV/AIDS charities in the city. This eventually led to me setting up an unofficial event company. I raised over €10,000 for three charities by the time I was twenty. I've often wondered if the lower levels of dopamine that ADHD people are rumoured to have meant I was constantly thrill-seeking by experiencing the rush of organising large-scale events. Obviously, the aspect of hyperfocus is incredibly useful in that kind of element, but it has a downside. It also means that stuff not in your line of sight gets left behind.

My schoolwork inevitably took a dive, and I

flunked out. It was hard to be present in class when I'd been up late writing press releases or holding photo calls. I ran from meeting to meeting and was never able to create any decent art because I wasn't there to do it. Suddenly I went from a student having a ball and organising a zillion things to a full-time shop assistant at Topshop. My ADHD meant I was stretching myself far too thin by signing up for everything. I begged to be let back in and thankfully, they allowed it but only with strict agreement that the distractions had to stop.

I did what I needed to do. I focused on my studies and managed to get through college. It wasn't fun or easy but somehow, the year and a half that I had left melted away and suddenly, I was good to graduate and get a job. But Ireland had other plans for me towards the end of my art college days in 2008.

I graduated into a changed Ireland. The arse fell out of the economy. The Celtic Tiger was long dead and stalking the ghost estates that littered the country. The money I had grown up to expect would always be there vanished, taking a lot of jobs with it. I panicked as the jobs dried up and earning money became difficult.

I eventually got a job in Arnotts department store in Dublin, which was most definitely not where I wanted to be. One day, I randomly walked into an open day for a college and somehow ended up on a Master's degree in Journalism. I had started writing online during my last years of art college though I never expected anyone to read my words. However, my blog, a rare thing in 2008, became oddly successful. I talked about fashion and beauty against a backdrop of personal stories about my friends.

My years in Dublin defined much of who I am today. I stayed out late, I drank wine from cartons, and I smoked packets upon packets of Marlboro Lights. My flat, a crumbling apartment on Fitzwilliam Square, was bankrupting me but I didn't care, because it was staggering distance to the bars where I went frequently dressed in my finest sequins and whatever tat I'd acquired that week. So what if there was no central heating and a broken window which nearly killed me during that snow-filled winter? I was saving a fortune in travel. I'd laugh with all the lads over drinks in town then go home to lay in bed in a winter coat under my duvet. I fell asleep in the Arnotts' staff canteen a few times over my media law notes, only coming to when the staff would bang trays loudly.

There wasn't a sniff of a job during those days and everyone I knew was side hustling. We all had one or six as we tried to keep the lights on. I would work retail with people who were stylists for celebrities in their free time. Hyperactivity is made for moonlighting, because most ADHD people love the thrill of the chase when it comes to having multiple jobs.

That also went for partying, which created opportunities to network among other people in fashion and media. All of us descended on the same nightclub on Thursdays and Fridays, as if it was church. My constant search for a dopamine fix and a good tune or two would keep me dancing till dawn, then it was a quick run home for coffee and a smoke before heading back to Arnotts. I'd often shake the glitter out of my mane while talking to customers about their outfits.

Meanwhile, my focus was everywhere but on my life, and that was a mess. I knew no limits to the alcohol and certainly didn't recognise when to go to bed. I flew through my wages weekly, often reaching into my overdraft when I hit rock bottom and rent was due. The cost of ADHD when it comes to money management is shocking thanks to our love of risky behaviours.

But it was becoming increasingly obvious that I needed a job that paid me more than peanuts. I'm not going to pretend that I fell into journalism because I had to fight tooth and nail for it. All media roads lead to Dublin in Ireland, and the capital city does not like the sound of rural voices. Rural voices are often seen as something to mock, or we're held up as thick. I once had a station manager turn to me and say, "You don't sound very West Cork, but that will make it easier for you to get a job." I'm embarrassed to say that I was almost grateful for that as it passed for nice in Dublin media circles.

At a radio station job that I had, I sat in the newsroom while two men shouted over my head about the women they'd been having sex with. The thought that I was presenting as female at that time and might be offended by their chat clearly hadn't occurred to either of them.

I think my ODD kicked in a little bit when I decided that I wasn't going to be ignored, and I was going to force the media to accept me, even if it didn't want to. I've fought really hard to get the most complex topics into the media ever since, from gay sex to drugs to abortion law, all in my West Cork accent. Although I may have lost my accent somewhat in the years since I left, I write rural and always will do.

Around this time, my days off were filled with college, my thesis, my blog, filing copy, and applying for internships. The internships were all Ireland had for us. We were deeply into bailouts at this stage, and my generation were thrown to wolves. We started emigrating in droves to escape, but I tried my best to stay for as long as I could. I'd spent a little bit too long believing that the Celtic Tiger would eventually roar again and leaning into the mysticism that all I had to do was work hard and I'd get the golden job I had been promised was out there.

My blog started to demand more and more of my time. For something that had begun its life as a joke, it was now bringing in invites to press days, collection launches, and even London Fashion Week, which I couldn't afford to attend. As the viewing figures grew, I sat on the front row of Brown Thomas fashion shows, being filmed by TV3, wearing Yves Saint Laurent that I had pinched off a stylist I knew. I got given incredibly expensive press gifts, which I wore with clothing I had bought on sale in Topshop. It was a weird time where the traditional press was deeply suspicious of anyone who worked online, especially bloggers. We were seen as a mad species of journalist yet regarded as royalty by PR girls who recognised the way the wind was blowing. They knew the tide was turning and that bloggers would do the same write-up as a journalist for a lot less money, or even just perks. Still, I'll never forget the look of surprise on my Dublin editor's face when I turned up at a high-profile fashion event in the Irish Museum of Modern Art, having been invited because of my blog instead of the magazine I worked with.

My ADHD came in handy when it came to work. My hyperactivity meant I could hold down several jobs at once, often running from one to another on little sleep, a few smokes, and no food. It was an exciting time when Dublin seemed alive with possibility.

There was a crippling recession which meant there were no jobs, no futures, no careers, and no money to be had but out of that environment came glorious creativity. Everyone I knew was creating something, from art to film to writing. People I had gone to college with were becoming famous for their art or performances. However, there were a lot of doors slammed shut on us when we asked to be paid for our work or to have proper hours on our contract. I remember being asked to do the makeup for a film by a director. The film would be shot in Malahide over three days. I was expected to do this for free, which I'm ashamed to say that I did.

I kept on pushing by introducing myself and networking. My ADHD mind was constantly seeking the dopamine buzz of working on creative projects. I didn't have the physical energy to back up all this creative mental energy; I simply said yes to everything I could, whether it was viable or not. I ended up working for free for a lot of radio and publications across Dublin. I lost my apartment as my job went under. I took a risk I hadn't calculated properly and started working for an Irish designer who was notoriously bad at paying her staff. On more than one occasion, I ran to her Thomas Street office to collect cheques that would bounce. I gave up the flat and started sleeping on couches of friends with enough clothes for the week in a backpack. It became a common sight to find me asleep in the college newsroom on one of the big leather couches with my coat thrown over me. This was my first real example of the exhaustion that can come from overworking as an ADHD person. What goes up has to come back down, and I crash landed with a thud. I spent so long chasing the dopamine buzz that comes with work and deadlines that I hadn't noticed I wasn't sleeping or eating properly. I dropped from a size twelve to a size six and looked gaunt. I swayed when I stood up, and I started to make very little sense when I spoke. It was a frightening development, and one that was only remedied by starting to eat properly and quitting some of the jobs that I'd accepted.

One thing I couldn't quite quit was the blogging thing that had taken over, and it had major perks. Sometimes, the only way I could afford to have a dinner that wasn't slices of plastic cheese on rice cakes was to go to press events. I would be champagne drunk on a Buckfast budget at events in places like Brown Thomas. I would make my notes, take my photos, and get whatever coverage I needed before finally giving in and getting a bit tipsy on the alcohol they were offering. The Irish fashion crowd were starting to become familiar faces, but it was always the same type of person that I met at these events: wealthy, white, and straight women. Dishevelled blond extensions, fake tans, and huge handbags balanced on the crook of their arm defined them as a group. I think they would have died to know I unofficially had no place of my own to burn the luxury candles they gave me in the goody bags. I was finding that, yet again, this was another place that I just didn't fit in. My queerness and my ADHD made me look and feel different from the other people who seemed to effortlessly understand how all this worked.

I took full advantage of the free food and drink while I could. Thank god, my policy has always been to get the work done first and never drink or eat to excess in front of people you work with or for. I never did anything mortifying. Although while at a TV3 travel show which my friend Zoe and I had gone to for the free goods, I was plonked in front of the presenters for an impromptu interview. I had no interest in the show I was technically there to watch so hadn't bothered to learn their names or take note of who they were. This was immediately evident when my opening line was, "Ah, it's yourself…the guy off the telly." He took it well.

Journalism isn't easy to get into but it's thrilling. I often think it's the best possible job for ADHD folk. You can obsessively focus on one story before switching to another. Your ability to take late nights, lack of food, and fascination with finding new and exciting stories is welcomed.

But as I started my journalism career, I was in Dublin and beginning to realise that Ireland wasn't going to properly employ me. It was time to go. I'd stayed too long at the party; the lights were coming up around me and guests were leaving.

So I packed up, and I started a new life in Nottingham.

Chapter Two
Sex, Love, and...Adult ADHD

But what about love? If ADHD had been influencing my work life and friendships to the extent that I've written almost an entire chapter about it, then surely my love life must have been affected too. It was. But it would be another ten years before I realised or admitted it to myself.

I was at college when ADHD first started to affect my relationships. I had met F on a night out to Costello's while I was still in art college. They were singing "99 problems" by Jay-Z in a drunken state on the walk to the club. So I joined them, roaring "BUT A BITCH AIN'T ONE," while we shared a stolen can, and I took sips shyly while we stole glances at each other.

We were together for about three years before I came out as queer. I identified for a time as bisexual and dated men, although that's no longer the case. F was my first proper love and made me feel so safe and secure, but all the distraction and the hyperfocus I was giving to the events I was working on translated into less attention on them. I had yet to learn what hyposexuality was and when our sex life plummeted into nothing, I had no words for it other than, "It's not you. I swear." I purchased sexy lingerie and every couples' sex toy I could find. We tried threesomes. Nothing worked.

Sex became the elephant in the room. We knew it was there or rather, it wasn't there. No one spoke about it. We just carried on being together and loving each other, but there was no sex. This would form a pattern.

There were other factors to the lack of sex that need inclusion here. We were living under the repression of the eighth amendment, which forbade abortion in Ireland. "Going to England for the weekend" was commonplace and scary. It meant funds we didn't have for operations we were told were immoral. The fear of pregnancy led to the break in your pill packet being accompanied by a chorus of, "Oh god, oh please, fuck, fuck, fuck, please," before it started and you could breathe again.

I did a lot of sexual experimentation in college, which is what it's for. (Well, it's for other things too, but I'm sure that's one of them.) I worked in a sex shop for two years with discounts on lube, dildos, and handcuffs. F wasn't my only partner in art college because we split before my final year. However, for the patience and kindness they showed me, they are the only one worth mentioning.

F had been respectful, but I quickly learned that not all men were. I had a new partner, G, who was a history student, an extremely hard worker who was completely dedicated to their study. G and I were plagued by the same sexual dysfunction that had affected my relationship with F. They wanted it, and they weren't at all respectful of me not wanting it. They once hurt me so badly during anal sex that I curled up in a small ball, jamming bed clothes into my mouth to stop from making sounds while I cried silent tears. They had pushed me into trying anal sex after badgering me for weeks to try it. They only stopped begging for sex if there was a reason like a headache, period, or other tangible physical proof that I was out of action for the night.

There was such a period of panic attached to this time that I didn't think that my body worked properly. The panic was also attached to a sense of relief whenever I managed to get through another night without sex. Confused, I hadn't thought that my lack of interest in sex might be attached to my ADHD, which meant I grasped at any other explanation for it, including asexuality and depression.

While I've had plenty of short, light-hearted affairs with highly inappropriate people, there are two that have been the closest I've come to finding a soul mate. I've used a lot of examples of my relationships in this book, but these two are the best ones I have for describing the incredible connection you can have with other neurodivergent people, and the slow but steady way love can develop with neurotypicals. Neither had an advantage over the other and neither worked out.

So you may as well know how I met both of them.

"New York, I love you, but you're bringing me down." ADHD Meets ADHD

I met S when I was still a broke art student, and he was a DJ. He was intoxicating, obsessive, annoying, and he drove me mad. I was so heartbreakingly in love with him but at the same time, I recognised bad behaviour when I saw it.

We were an immediate item. We met when my friend D and I ended up outside Costello's bar in Limerick, all dressed up with our plastic bag of takeaway beers ready to go. It was after the club had emptied out for the night, and we were looking for an after-party. I was about to give up when D shouted at a man across the street.

"Ah, Jesus, is that SK?" she screamed (using his full name). But before I could clock who she was shouting at, she had taken off towards him. S was tall and incredibly thin. He had the sort of body that's made for skinny jeans. He was all leather jacket and Marlboro Lights, with the most piercing blue eyes, like they could cut through you.

"D, how's things?" He laughed, but his light blue eyes stared into mine.

His attention made me uncomfortable. Who was this man? He took us to a house party somewhere in the city. From the moment I sat down beside him, we didn't stop talking. There was an electrical charge in the air that was impossible to describe. I learned that he was a DJ in the city with a part-time bar job on the side. He was a lot older than me, approaching his forties to my mid-twenties, but he seemed closer to my age in the way he carried himself.

He was a chronic smoker and lit one smoke off another, offering me one each time. As a broke student, cigarettes were a luxury I wasn't really able to afford, so I helped him through his supply while we tore through our cans of cider.

No subject was off limits as we sailed through music (indie), politics (not Fianna Fáil or Fine Gael), plans for the future (residencies abroad and graduations) before moving into more serious topics of dating. I told him I was in a relationship with a boy I wasn't interested in, and that reminded me that I hadn't thought of him or texted him all evening. I continued not thinking about him when S kissed me and asked for my number. The connection was instant, and I didn't entertain the idea of not seeing him again for a second. I knew I had to.

While he told me he suspected he had ADHD, he hadn't formally been diagnosed at that stage. His behaviour was classic and mirrored my own. S followed me from art college to my master's, and then to Nottingham when I emigrated. Our relationship was always on again-off again, and every time he left me, I would run away to start a new life in a new city, claiming, "This is it, and I mean it this time. He's finally done it." In reality, that just meant I was going to eventually forgive him and take him back for the next seven years.

S would always find me again and again, no matter where I went. He sent a simple message on Facebook that said, "I'm sorry," for his usual ghosting or infraction that had torn us apart. The message would pop up on my screen begging to be seen and dealt with. There would be a second message: "I owe you a better explanation and a lunch." Followed by a third: "I don't expect you to ever speak to me again." I, weakened by my loneliness, wouldn't be able to stand it anymore and always messaged back: "You don't owe me a lunch, but the apology would be welcome."

That was it. I was stuck again for the next two years.

He, alone and living in New York and I, alone and living in Nottingham, communicated across social media in a wave of messages. His ADHD drove me mad but excited me. He knew all the best bars and places to go. He marched to the beat of the same extra fast drum I did, and his energy fed mine. We drove each other mad with our insatiable appetite for fun. We would start at one bar for a drink before one of us would say, "Wait, I know where we should go," and that would continue until it was three a.m., and we were on a rooftop with bottles of Bulmers in Brooklyn. He knew what it felt like to have a vibrant energy that constantly pulsates through the body. I'd never met anyone who knew what that felt like, and there was a joy in not having to explain why I couldn't sit still or needed to go clubbing on Tuesday at noon.

But this feeling came at a price. He was an emotional vampire when he was low. He sought out people with excessive energy to feed from. Unsurprisingly, I was always exhausted when S would eventually leave me.

We would wake up in a hungover heap after the night before, and he would light one cigarette for me before another for himself. The smoke curled upwards as we huddled together under the daylight seeping from under the curtains. The city that never sleeps is perfect for ADHD people. It seems as if the city is looking for the same spare dopamine that we are. We bounced from bar to bar pushing the limits of our sleeplessness as far we dared to go.

But I was slowing down and starting to harness my ADHD hyperfocus to my career. I still loved the bars, but it was getting harder to be out all night. I wanted him to stop and slow down with me. His ADHD couldn't stop, though, and when his age made him slow down, he topped his energy levels with cocaine. (I wouldn't realise until much later in life that he'd been on coke and took so much, he often didn't pay his rent. I'd assumed his constant motion was like mine—all down to the function of our neurodiverse systems).

Sometimes, it isn't about the ADHD. You can just be wrong for each other.

We did not go gently into that good night. Our relationship had been a car crash from the start, so it was inevitable that our breakup would be too. We spanned years of them but eventually, we reached a point where the worst finally came knocking at the door.

Neither of us recognised that our ADHD traits combined meant we were feeding off each other like vampires. I always recognised him engaging in this behaviour without acknowledging mine. In suffering the dopamine deficiency that we do, we craved the stimulation of being each other's bad influence. "Drinks on a Wednesday night when we have work the next day?" We would laugh. "But of course. Bring it."

I didn't need a licensed professional to tell me that S wasn't good for me, but I did need a life coach to fill in the surprising blanks about how it had gone on for so long. We can't regulate our emotions in the same way that neurotypicals can, so we feel everything deeply. S and I were ADHD emotional empaths who had surprising depths for two people who loved vodka shots and cigarettes so much.

When S finally left me, it was because he was an ADHD man struggling to cope with various life changes, and when he was overwhelmed, he shut down completely. He simply couldn't carry on.

Our final night was a week before Valentine's Day when I was sitting outside on the stoop that led to my front door. I was smoking which, at that time, was a constant fixture in my life. A cold silence had descended over my phone. It had been three days of his complete communication blackout, which normally signalled he was about to detach from me again where he would not text, message, or answer my calls. As I sat on the stoop of my bedsit, I read on Facebook that he had gone back to New York. I don't know why I was surprised as he had a strange, abusive relationship with the city. New York was his one true love and no matter how bad it got, he always went back.

He would promise me the world, only to back out last minute when he realised what the world would cost him. My texts, calls, and prayers would go unanswered as I begged him to let me know he was alive at least. I began to internalise the behaviours as his way of telling me I was unlovable. I believed his disappearance was because I was a bad person, and no one would ever want to be with me again. I started going on long walks, where I would run through everything in my mind over and over in case I'd missed a message or a sign.

ADDitude magazine ran a blog post on this kind of behaviour. Beth Main wrote, "Obsessing and ruminating are often part of living with ADHD. No matter how hard you try to ignore them, those negative thoughts just keep coming back, replaying themselves in an infinite loop. You know it's not healthy, but you can't seem to stop yourself. As adults with ADHD, we're so often burned by our own impulsivity that we sometimes go to the opposite extreme and micro-analyse. Our minds are always on, often running laps around the same track."[1]

S and I were running a marathon neither of us

could win. We didn't even know we were running.
We were engaging in a cycle of bad behaviour.
S would disappear when he was overwhelmed, I
would internalise and become obsessed with why,
allowing me to engage in rumination, then S would
feel guilty and come back. I would relapse into
forgiveness, because it gave me validation that I
couldn't possibly have been that bad. After all, he
came back, didn't he?

There had been a lot leading up to that day
where I sat on the steps smoking. We had been to
Skegness together on a day trip when S was visiting
to look for work in Nottingham. He'd moved back
from New York to Ireland, and I thought he would
move in with me. The job search wasn't going well;
the only work on offer was miles below the cool
DJ and sound engineer jobs he'd worked in New
York. He had spent nights chasing the dopamine
hit of building an energy level at the clubs across
Manhattan, so the idea of a desk job was destroying
him. On the way home, ice cream in hand, I asked
him casually when he thought he would move in.

"Ah, you know, it all depends on work really…
Sure, I can't be leaving Mam to look after herself
either…"

It flashed into my head that this hadn't bothered
him when he ran away to New York in the first place,
but I shrugged it off. He vanished shortly after that.

On the stoop, I opened Facebook and the status
update popped up almost immediately. *S lives in
New York.* Had he really gone back to America
without telling me? It was now or never. I went cold
turkey and haven't spoken to him since. I don't
believe he's a bad person, but it took me five years
to be able to say that.

While researching this book, I spoke to many different ADHD people and professionals who deal with neurodiversity. The notion of an ADHD life coach was a new one, given that there were none of those in rural Cork when I was growing up. A mutual friend introduced me to Anastacia Galadza, a Canadian ADHD life coach. We immediately set about a series of chats over Zoom. Pandemic aside, there was sadly no way of my travelling to Canada to have a conversation in person.

"The ADHD overwhelming and disappearing thing is not a commitment thing," Anastasia explained. "It's definitely neurobiological, and that's something people need to be aware of in themselves. If your traits don't balance each other out, then that can be problematic. You can have successful ADHD/ADHD relationships, but it depends on what their traits look like. Introverted, inattentive traits can balance well with a person who is more extroverted and is your opposite."

She added, "This can happen neurotypically, but there is the intensity and the stimulation of finding the craziness and feeding off each other's energy. Going out to find the best bars and partying can be really stimulating in terms of dopamine hits which is what the ADHD brain craves."

After that vanishing act, I tore myself apart mentally and physically. I detoxed from him by quitting everything that I had in my life, from cigarettes to my job to my terrible apartment. I disappeared by running away from my failing life to Italy, where I remained for a year licking my wounds and rebuilding myself.

When I landed a job teaching English as a second language in Italy, I failed to recognise the running away as an ADHD thing—me seeking out a dopamine hit and avoiding conflict. I wanted to top up my extremely low post-break up dopamine by cutting all ties and escaping to a new city to start again, which I had done many times before. An all or nothing response was just another day and is incredibly typical for ADHD folk.

Italy was gorgeous. Just mind-blowing gorgeousness everywhere you looked. The small city I lived in was more like a sleepy town. I loved my life there. I rented a very basic apartment next door to the small school I taught at. The doorway had marble steps and a huge wisteria plant hung over the entrance. In the spring, I would sit outside with a coffee on those steps to read while the gorgeous flowers swayed over my head. Eventually I gave up playing it cool with the city and just fell in love by giving in to how beautiful it was.

Stepping into the classroom was an utterly terrifying experience. The course I chose to do didn't prepare me for entering a room full of tiny faces looking up at me expectantly. I wasn't used to being a trusted adult, and I'm pretty sure that showed immediately. I don't think I ever felt comfortable, especially because traditional teaching doesn't come naturally to me. The fact that my own educational experience was akin to dentistry without anaesthesia probably didn't help. I'm terrible with discipline and eventually the kids figured it out.

So if S was the first person you need to know about then R is the second person I should introduce you to. Post-Italy and successfully detoxed from S, I was a different person. As he left my system for good, I felt ready to take on a relationship again.

ADHD and Neurotypical

I stood in the busy bar pretending to be more confident than I felt. I tried to keep my focus on what I was ordering instead of looking around me to try and clock my date. It was a gloomy, random school night in November, and I was on the worst type of date—a first one. I hadn't officially met her yet, because I'd arrived first and that gave me the chance to have at least a pint of panic wine.

I had been swapping text messages back and forth with R after we connected on Tinder. There is nothing scarier than a first date with a new potential interest where you have to decide if they are in real life normal or not.

I'd also had the worst day at work, which saw me cry most of my foundation off in the bathroom due to stress. I'm not in the humour for any of this but here I am at the bar, waiting.

I'd ordered a large wine when I hear a small voice to my left, "C?"

I was relieved to see she looked in real life normal when I turned to greet her. She was shorter than me with a cropped, dark bob. Her outfit said professional but quirky, highlighted by a pair of silver glittery socks that were on display under her cropped skinny jeans. We order another wine (also large) and sit down.

She laughed, cracked jokes, and was easy to talk to so. In many ways, I felt like I'd hit the jackpot. I picked up on the fact that she wasn't super experienced with queer relationships but then, neither was I. A lot of her stories about being out of the closet seemed recent so I guessed it hadn't been long for her. She was also in her late twenties in comparison to my mid-thirties, which didn't seem like too bad a gap.

There was a bit of flirtation and two more wines (again large) before we eventually called it a night. While there wasn't an immediate attraction, I was intrigued enough to ask her out for another date.

After that night, we were inseparable for the next two years. We were a fixture at events around Nottingham from films to drag shows while I wrote a column about my gallivanting around the city. I often referenced R in these short, almost diary-like entries. Her serious yet quiet self suited my over-the-top personality enough. I pushed her out of her comfort zone, and she reined me back into mine.

I was so used to the instant car crash from dating S that the quiet, real love I experienced with R took me by complete surprise. It was the closest I ever felt to being completely myself around another human being, and it took time to develop into something serious. It also gave me the balance and grounding to start feeling secure about my sexuality, so I naturally used this to start asking a million questions about my gender, which I was less than secure about.

All of our firsts took time, but it didn't matter because I think we instinctively knew we weren't going anywhere fast, and that this wasn't a short-term thing.

We waited three days before our first kiss which was outside the Megaclose student accommodation building by Victoria Centre. I am nothing if not a romantic who picks the perfect setting to ask if I can kiss someone for the first time. Our first "I love you'" was less of a moment but was something that slipped into our conversations with ease as if it'd always been there. We met families, extended families for dinners, drives, coffees, and birthdays. She came to Dublin and met my *everyone* in one go, and I beamed when they loved her as much as I did. I caught a confirmation nod over her head from time to time as she passed assessments.

I began to think about the future in a way that didn't fill me with dread. I made plans to buy my first home and asked her to move in with me when I bought it. Suddenly the world was full of matching towel sets, toasters that did four slices of bread, and IKEA. There were so many trips to IKEA in her vintage and battered two-door, dark green car where we shared meatballs and debated a double Idanäs.

There was just one small problem that both of us were great at ignoring—we never had sex. The relationship issues that had plagued me throughout my twenties had come back, and I was once again avoiding sex or any intimacy. What did it matter, right? I felt guilty, because we had all the love and affection for each other you could possibly want.

I began to plan to propose to R almost as a way of ensuring she didn't leave me, and also because I felt it was the logical next step. I chose my place, my time, my outfit, what I would say but thank god for small mercies, I didn't choose the ring. I planned to ask at her looming thirtieth birthday in one of my favourite places. But a visit to Stockholm in November proved frostier than just the weather, and I started to realise we wouldn't make it that far.

Many weeks and a global pandemic later, we were deep into lockdown when we spent our first night together in the house. She hadn't moved in but then, I'd only barely moved in. We shared a bottle of gin while watching TV sitting on the floor, in lieu of chairs. Something had been bothering me, and I wasn't about to let it go. In typical ADHD lack of filters-style, I blurted it out. "You haven't moved anything in yet. Are you still planning to? Tell me I'm being paranoid here."

I knew I wasn't.

I'd taken empty IKEA moving boxes to her house after I'd emptied them. The boxes had sat there, still empty, tucked away in various rooms waiting to be filled. Apart from her culling her book collection, I hadn't seen her pack anything. I had one single shelf of her books in the house and nothing else. I had caught her housemate resting her feet on one of the boxes when I'd called round to collect R before heading home. After four weeks of excuses for not moving, I knew it was time to bring it up. I couldn't simply avoid it and pretend things were okay the way I had with S. It was a moment of growth, though I didn't recognise it at the time.

Her expression told me I was right. Her face was filled with guilt and relief, like she'd known this conversation was coming.

She sighed deeply. "Okay, I promise I was going to talk to you about this. It's just been a lot with the pandemic and all," she said. "I'm not sure it's a good time for things like this. It's a big step, and we don't know what's going to happen with lockdown yet."

She played with the tassels on a cushion and wouldn't look at me directly. She said it wasn't personal, but how could it not be? I stood up and ran my hands through my hair. "You've known for months that this was coming. You've been planning to move in here for six months. You bought the microwave and the fucking towels," I said. There was silence while we gathered our thoughts. While the fight we had was small and over quickly, the hurt and damage done was instantly clear. She went to work, and I got ready to do more painting.

While painting, I realised that we hadn't been working for months. There was no denying that we loved each other immensely, but we weren't having sex and things had felt off for a while. I violently slapped the forest green paint across the wall in big splattering arches. We weren't even that affectionate anymore. I painted FUCK in big letters on the wall before covering it. Our Halloween trip to Stockholm hadn't been the first warning sign but the second or even the third. We'd had a fight on our last night which saw her go to the palace alone while I drank coffee in the old quarter. The fight had been over sex or the apparent lack of it. I started to feel the first stirrings of *Something Isn't Right Here And You Know It* before I shoved it down as far as I could. I'd ignored the red flag because I hadn't wanted to acknowledge the problem. That evening was the result.

I saw the writing on the wall clearly, and I'm not talking about the FUCK I had painted there. I knew we weren't suited, and I was going to leave her. I was ready to settle down, have a small family of kittens, and live with a partner. R was in her late twenties and not at that stage yet. When I was her age, I was being irresponsible in Nottingham and celebrating life with a series of late nights, bad decisions, and even worse dates. She deserved to have those remaining years of madness before she got to the same stage I was. She was too young for me.

Why hadn't anyone told me?

As I recovered from my breakup with R, my mind drifted to how ADHD could be affecting the sex and relationships I had. I started to research and quickly saw my relationships reflected in my research about hyposexuality, hyperfocus, romantic focus, and kink.

For the first time, I realised my ADHD could be having an effect on my sex life. I wanted to cry or scream, because it should have been explained to me. Shouldn't it?

The Gender Gap

One of the reasons that it was never really explained to me might be because of something called the gender gap, which can affect everything from medical diagnosis to the data on file for different conditions.

It's extremely complex, but at some point it was determined that people who might be able to have children and were of childbearing age were too unstable to participate in studies because of fluctuating hormones or the potential to get pregnant. This means that studies, drugs, and diagnostic tests are normally designed for and tested on men. You will also notice that while there is little out there for women on ADHD, there is absolutely nothing for non-binary or transgender folk on the subject.

In the book, *Invisible Women: Exposing Data Bias in a World Designed for Men*, Caroline Criado Perez talks about how the gender data gap presents huge, and sometimes deadly, issues for women. It also mentions how the socialisation of women and cultural differences can contribute to the misdiagnosis of autism and ADHD.

"For years we thought that autism is four times more common in boys than girls, and that when girls have it, they are more seriously affected. But new research suggests that in fact female socialisation may help girls mask their symptoms better than boys and that there are far more girls living with autism than we previously realised...This historical failure is partly a result of the criteria for diagnosing having been based on data 'derived almost entirely from studies of boys.'"

Caroline makes a similar point with ADHD: "There are similar diagnostic problems when it comes to attention deficit hyperactive disorder (ADHD) and Aspergers. Up to three quarters of girls with ADHD are estimated to be undiagnosed—a gap which Ellen Littman, the author of *Understanding Girls with ADHD*, puts down to the early clinical studies of ADHD being done on 'really hyperactive young white boys.' Girls tend to present less as hyperactive and more as disorganised, scattered, and introverted."[2]

I ran away to Italy after my breakup, but I chose to return to Nottingham after a year. While I loved Italy, my father had gotten sick, and I wanted to be closer to home. There was also the matter of wanting to put down roots somewhere as the travel lifestyle was getting to me. I just *existed* in the apartment in Italy, and it wasn't home. It had done what I needed it to do, though. I'd healed from my broken relationship and had begun to focus on myself and who I wanted to be. I was determined to start a career that would mean I left makeup artistry for good.

Nottingham had changed while I was away.

The life I had left behind had been full of drunk DIY gigs, smoking, and run-down apartments. The city had new shops, restaurants, and places I'd never seen. The life I left was gone; friends were in rehab, had quit smoking, replaced those run-down apartments with family-sized homes and filled them with family. It was now less about the Friday night beers in Rough Trade and more about trips to B&Q or weddings. How had so much changed in such a short space of time?

ADHD folk don't deal well with change. I felt out of my depth as I tried to pick up the threads of my old life. Some friendships never properly recovered from my leaving and remain shattered to this day. Eventually, I carved out a new life for myself and met new people. I gradually began to take on work as a journalist in the city. I got my radio show back and wrote for local magazines again. As difficult as it was, I held onto the vision of myself I'd had in Italy and took it day by day.

I kept up my ADHD research. I joined support groups which showed me other LGBT+ people were experiencing these things too. I read studies where I really had to force myself to understand the complex wording. I started to write about ADHD. I had been quiet long enough about being neurodiverse but now I started to sound like a broken record, harping on about it to everyone who would listen. I collected a group of ADHD women and non-binary/trans people to talk to me about their sex lives, relationships, and their diagnoses to confirm I wasn't going mad. When their discussions and answers came back confirming my theories, I was delighted. I finally had confirmation that it wasn't just me.

I told employers about my condition too. As a former makeup artist and now a journalist, I realised how my ADHD affects my work, and this is more obvious in an office setting. Given that makeup artistry was full of creative, strange folk like me, it was easier to hide my ADHD behind a veneer of being oddly colourful. I never spent longer than an hour with a client, so it was never obvious. However, my inattentiveness and sequencing issues are *very* obvious when you're reading my work. I once heard that the journalist, AA Gill, had to have all his articles transcribed because of his serious dyslexia, which fills me with hope. Whatever your feelings on AA Gill, if newspapers can make that kind of allowance for someone neurodiverse in that way, then they can accommodate ADHD generally. But I grew tired of having to explain why sometimes things are harder for me than my neurotypical colleagues. I also think in the case of one company in particular, it was a contributing factor to me losing the job.

We, collectively, as ADHD women, or non-binary, or transgender people need to be louder about where we struggle in comparison to neurotypical folk. We also need to talk to each other to make sure we're supported. If we don't, then we risk not being included in the research, which means we don't get support services that work for us. They will carry on catering to the same people they always have. Eventually, I went on to speak to other people with ADHD who would go quiet when I told them things about it. No one had explained what was going on to them either.

So here we are.

Chapter Three
What is ADHD anyway?

Before things move on a bit more, I'd like to take this opportunity to state here and now that I am not a doctor or psychiatrist of *any* description; I'm simply a person who was diagnosed as ADHD at the age of eleven and has been pretty much ignored by doctors and psychiatrists of all descriptions ever since. I've spent a lot of time pretending I don't have ADHD and that I'm just fine without any extra help when, clearly, I am not.

Everyone has different levels of understanding about ADHD. This chapter is dedicated to giving us all the same knowledge before we get into the more difficult stuff. Some may have picked this up fresh from an adult diagnosis or others may have bought this for a bewildered loved one who is trying to understand a neurodiverse partner. Whatever your level or starting point, I'm going to attempt to make sure we all know our ADHD from our RSD (Rejection Sensitivity Disorder).

If you suspect while reading this that you may be ADHD but are undiagnosed, for the love of all that is holy, please *don't* diagnose yourself with this book. Please go and get help from your GP, or your family, or educational resources.

If you suspect a loved one has ADHD, but they haven't got a diagnosis or they haven't mentioned it, don't be a dick. Don't diagnose someone else. It's not your place to do that. Encourage them to get help and talk to someone only if they express an interest or concern to you first. It's rude and can be traumatic to assume you know that someone is ADHD or has any form of neurodiversity.

Also, people don't necessarily need a diagnosis of ADHD. It might not be the right thing for them, and it's a personal choice to seek one out. The wait times for the NHS services and the cost of a private assessment can make this a difficult personal choice and one where access is an issue. Meanwhile, people can decide they don't need it, don't want to know, or would prefer to educate themselves on what their ADHD looks like.

That said, here we go with some of the straightforward questions about ADHD.

What is ADHD?

Attention Deficit Hyperactive Disorder (ADHD) is classed as a condition that can affect people's behaviour according to the National Health Service (the trusty NHS). They reckon that people can seem restless, have trouble concentrating, and act on impulse. As ADHD is a developmental disorder, it's believed that it cannot develop in adults without first appearing in childhood.

My poor mother will back that claim up. I wasn't the easiest of children to control or parent. I was horrendously difficult on occasion and could be violent as I struggled to regulate my emotions or frustration.

This scratches the surface of a more complex condition than people give it credit for. I'm sure that you all know the cliché of an ADHD teenager being unable to sit still or concentrate, but it's so much more than that. It's usually the stereotype of a boy too, as girls are often passed over in diagnosis.

I must admit, I struggle with referring to ADHD as a *condition* with *symptoms* that need *diagnosing* when to me, it's just how my brain is. But for the book, I'll use this terminology here and there, since it's all we have at the moment. Some of the studies and books I quote from may still use this terminology too as it's quite recent thinking that hasn't been fully adopted yet.

A parent survey from 2016 to 2019 by the US Centers for Disease Control (CDC) found that boys are much more likely to have ever been diagnosed as ADHD than girls. These studies are always divided into binary groups of boys and girls or men and women. I have yet to see studies where there's an inclusion of transgender or non-binary folks, so we have a lot of ground to cover in the future. The researchers estimated that it was 13% male to 6% female, which is a big gap in numbers. The highest age group for diagnosis in the same study was 12 to 17 years with 3.3 million cases.[3] That's a lot of fidget spinners.

Traditionally, and somewhat unfairly, it was thought that girls can present more with inattentive ADHD, which makes them more dreamy and quiet in comparison to "the lads," who are more vocal. This, according to the CEO of ADHD Ireland is why women and girls slip through the cracks of diagnosis. Are we actually shocked that diagnoses in women, girls, non-binary, or trans people are missed when so much of the check list for diagnosis is based on white, cisgendered men or boys?

In an interview with *Today FM* in 2022, CEO Ken Kilbride estimated that boys were still four times as likely to be diagnosed as girls. Note that this is all being discussed in terms of the binary genders... again.

"Women and girls have slipped through the cracks for the last twenty to thirty years. That's probably down to the fact that there's still a public perception about ADHD being young boys bouncing off walls. But we now know that ADHD is primarily genetically driven. Which means in terms of its presentation, it's 50% boys, 50% girls."[4]

He also added that women are better at masking ADHD then men. This definitely didn't apply to me; I spent 50% of my time being inattentive and dreamy and the remaining 50% being hyperactive as all hell and giving my mother a heart attack.

"So they can internalise their ADHD, and they can internalise their hyperactivity. So they're not showing it and presenting it. They may come across as more inattentive. So it's the shy girl down the back of the class who is not causing problems, staring out the window, not paying attention to their lessons. But they as much have ADHD as the boys do."

ADHD starts to show when we're kids. I was eleven when I was hauled in front of a specialist and diagnosed. My behaviour was monitored at school and home after that. I was also put on medication. It's not isolated to just kids though. While the NHS claims that some ADHD gets better with age, there are adults who continue to struggle later in life. They may also develop other conditions such as sleep issues, anxiety problems, and oppositional defiance disorder. I have all three of these, which is why I am such a catch and a pleasure to date. I know, I know. How am I single?

The NHS lists some traits of ADHD[5]:

- Having a short attention span and being easily distracted.
- Making careless mistakes—for example, in schoolwork.
- Appearing forgetful or losing things.
- Being unable to stick to tasks that are tedious or time-consuming.
- Appearing to be unable to listen to or carry out instructions.
- Constantly changing activity or task.
- Having difficulty organising tasks.
- Being unable to sit still, especially in calm or quiet surroundings.
- Constantly fidgeting.
- Being unable to concentrate on tasks.
- Excessive physical movement.
- Excessive talking (I often joke I don't come with an off switch or volume control).
- Being unable to wait their turn.
- Acting without thinking (I have at least two piercings that I attribute to this).
- Interrupting conversations.
- Little or no sense of danger (I used to hitch-hike around Ireland as a teenager. Enough said.)

Hyper Everything

Merriam Webster defines hyperactivity as:
1: the state or condition of being overly active
2: increased levels of function or activity especially when considered abnormally excessive

Hyperactivity affects everything from the way I eat to the way I work. I'm constantly in a rush to get to the next thing immediately which can manifest in twitching, excessive movement, and feeling actually pained at having to sit still. I physically feel a wired, low-level buzz of pulsating energy through my body at all times.

The cinema is a classic example. The minute I sit down to watch a film I've been raving about, I know I'm done. I feel panicked at the thought of sitting still for three hours and want to leave immediately, so I shift awkwardly in my chair, or need to scratch, or move my legs. As a child, I would twirl my fringe around my fingers, so I was still moving, and it was also self-soothing.

I don't have a volume control, off switch, or understanding of how to sit quietly or contain myself. I am the person who says the wrong thing in a rush to say the right one. I'm the person who runs out in the road because I haven't stopped to consider the cars. Hyperactivity means I don't sleep properly then go to work exhausted and run-down.

Is ADHD a Disability?

Yes.

There are lots of different words used to describe ADHD including condition, disability, disorder, and it's associated with words like diagnosis and symptoms. This can make it a bit confusing.

The Equality Act 2010 sets out when someone is considered to have a disability. The act states that someone is considered to have a disability if both of these statements apply:

- they have a "physical or mental impairment."

- the impairment "has a substantial and long-
  term adverse effect on their ability to carry out
  normal day-to-day activities."[6]

I think any ADHD person would agree with me
that it affects our ability to carry out our usual tasks.
I'm thinking in particular about me trying to lock
the front door of my house and not being able to,
because I can't process the sequence on how to lift
the handle and *then* twist the key.

People can feel a certain way about different
words though. Some are instantly horrendous to
all of us, but language changes quickly, meaning
people can get left behind when it comes to
updated words or terms. Some people prefer
disorder and won't use disabled, or the other way
around. I found, when interviewing people for this
book, that everyone had a different take, and that
can be a hot topic when discussing ADHD.

While writing this book, Mary Butler, the Fianna
Fáil Teachta Dála (TD) for Mental Health and
Older People in Ireland came out with interesting
language on Twitter. The words "altered ability"
were used to describe ADHD to a stunned
audience: "Honoured to launch the ADHD in Adults
National Clinical Programme Model of Care which
conceptualises ADHD as an altered ability rather
than a disability," she wrote.[7] There was uproar from
the ADHD community, myself included, although
she later apologised if it had been "misconstrued"
but failed to remove the tweet.

The community pointed out that to avoid using
the word disability is to diminish the experiences
that ADHD people go through every day. It sanitises
what is often a very tough thing to experience.

Those on Twitter also highlighted how serious this "altered ability" terminology could be when discussing disability support in terms of financial help or services. Are we excluded if these descriptions are used instead of the actual word? Butler was accused online of othering and ableism.

However, this is far from a unique experience. *The Irish Times* reported that when asked about schools for "children with additional needs" reopening amid the COVID-19 lockdowns, Josepha Madigan, Minister of State for Special Education and Inclusion made a slip in front of the press. She said, "We all know that even for normal children, remote teaching is difficult, but for children who have additional needs, it is particularly difficult."[8]

This type of language painting disabled people as different from "normal" people is depressing. It's extremely othering and worrying that there are politicians who view disability this way. Note, I said worrying but not surprising. In fairness, she later apologised, but this was an unscripted moment of press interaction. She only issued an apology when it was publicly pointed out why she was wrong.

In order to get a more varied viewpoint than my own, I went on a hunt to talk it over with other people. I reached out to interview non-binary artist Shar about being queer and ADHD. Shar lives in Ireland and makes a fantastic series on TikTok about ADHD. The subject of "altered abilities" versus disability came up as we chatted.

"The line about altered ability rather than disability comes from one of the people who organise the model of care, which I think is even more worrying as ADHD Ireland had it in the press release," they said. "I get them wanting to gate-keep the word disability, but there is no one way to be disabled. Even through my own internalised able-ism, I feel like it isn't my word to use. This has left me in a state where I'm not able to work, not able to do a lot that society expects from me. It is *disabling* me."

What Causes ADHD?

In short, no one knows. But there are a number of theories.

Apparently, it's genetic, so it can run in families. I'm adopted, so it would be difficult for me to prove that. I do know my biological family, so I guess it wouldn't be the worst thing to ask.

In fact, emboldened by the buzz of Irish cider when I was writing one time, I fired off a message to my biological sister. "Quick question, does anyone else in the family have ADHD? I do, and it's genetic, so I wondered." I then thoughtfully added, "How are you?" She typed back that no one else does. It's a big family, so how am I the only one? It's entirely possible I'm not; it's just that no one else has come forward to claim that particular identity.

Another theory is that it can be caused by low birth weights. I took another swig of room temperature cider and wrote to my adopted mother to ask if she knew what I weighed when I was born. "Was I a small or big child when I was born?" I typed quickly. She never replied.

The NHS helpfully suggests that it may be caused by an imbalance of neurotransmitter levels in the brain but less helpfully, does not link to these studies.

How Do You Get a Diagnosis?

My diagnosis was via a series of specialists in Cork City housed in identical, boring brown offices. While it was dull, it was also time out of school, so I wasn't completely against it.

I remember being driven to the city to see a specialist on a school day. It was a two-hour round trip, so my parents must have truly had enough of my behaviour at that stage to be venturing out of the wescht (how it sounds when someone from the west of Ireland says West). Trips to the city were truly a big occasion.

I don't recall much about this time, but I do remember being asked in one appointment to remember three words like ball, cat, and car. BALL. CAT. CAR. Or something like that. This was typical of the games that psychiatrists enjoyed playing with me. I love a challenge, so I was ready for him to ask me at the end of the appointment. I had been focusing on repeating the words over and over again in my mind throughout the appointment. BALL. CAT. CAR.

"That's all we have time for," he said, sliding papers into a folder.

What about the words? How could he have forgotten? "Weren't you meant to ask me about the words?" I asked, worried to be correcting an adult in case I got into trouble. "BALL. CAT. CAR," I repeated slowly as if talking to a child.

"I had completely forgotten to ask you." He glanced at my parents over my head.

I felt smug for having completed the task and won the imaginary prize I wasn't offered for having done so. Years later, knee-deep in research about

ADHD, I realised he hadn't forgotten. I think he was testing me to see if I had hyperfocus or not. He was also appealing to the ADHD need for a sense of achievement. We're platform gamers who love to complete a level with a clear sense of having won all the quests. The dopamine rush of completing a level and knowing you absolutely crushed every last task you needed to do makes all those hours spent sitting on your arse worth it.

My mother reminded me that I saw a total of three psychiatrists before eventually going private out of desperation. Apparently, the decision to go private came after a doctor told my mother that I would be dependent on them for care for the rest of my life and wouldn't amount to anything in life. I was misdiagnosed with bipolar disorder by that one psychiatrist, which could have had dangerous results if I'd been medicated. My parents felt the psychiatrist got the completely wrong impression of me and came out of the room absolutely furious. This, on top of the assessment from my school that I needed a good slap, was enough to frighten my parents into paying for a private assessment.

I'd hoped that this process had improved somewhat but sadly, a quick glance on social media tells me this isn't the case. As wait lists for the NHS surge, the idea of forgoing a diagnosis is growing, but for some within the community, the diagnosis matters and is worth the lengthy battle.

NHS Scotland outlines the lengthy process of getting diagnosed with ADHD. Individuals must have five or more symptoms of inattentiveness or five or more indicators of hyperactivity or impulsiveness.

"For an adult is diagnosed with ADHD when it's

considered that their symptoms have a moderate effect on their life. This can take the form of underachievement at or struggling to hold down a job, driving dangerously, and difficultly making or keeping friends. It can also mean difficulty in keeping partners."[9]

Oh, boy, do I know about those difficulties. My lack of acceptance or understanding of my own ADHD has cost me jobs, relationships, and friendships over the years like you wouldn't believe. And after seven months of learning to drive, I had to finally admit defeat as I was far too dangerous to be let loose on the roads. My ADHD caused me to make split-second decisions where I darted across lanes or overreacted to situations on the road. My job was dependent on me learning to drive so when I couldn't, it was gone. No excuses were accepted, so I was simply fired.

When it comes to relationships, I've dated neurotypical folk, and a lot of the time, they just didn't understand that I wasn't putting it on or exaggerating my ADHD traits. If one more neurotypical person suggests that they may have ADHD because they "cannot sit still," I'll scream. Try being made redundant because your brain doesn't behave or having your girlfriend leave you because you're "too much."

What is the Treatment?

I used to think I would take the blue pill in a second if it meant I woke up tomorrow without ADHD. But now, I'm not sure I want to. I've finally (sort of) embraced the positives while I learn to navigate the negatives. It's not my fault that the world is designed for neurotypicals. So much of this world is set up to serve binary ideas: straight, white, girl, boy… We now understand so much more about these things being on a spectrum, but society still makes us choose which colours we fit into without allowing for lots of overlap.

That isn't to say it's easy. It isn't. Many of my ADHD traits are both a blessing and a curse. On the one hand, I'm a chronic over-sharer of all the personal information no one asked for. I will tell you my life story for the price of a pint. On the flip side, I'm a good person whose dopamine-seeking means I know the best place to grab a pint, and my hyperfocus means I can turn out work very quickly. This comes in handy as a journalist when your editor needs emergency page-fillers as I flip copy incredibly fast. Would I want to be "treated" or "cured" if it were possible? I don't think so.

There is no cure for ADHD. According to the NHS, there are five medications in the UK to help control but not cure it:

- Methylphenidate
- Dexamfetamine
- Lisdexamfetamine
- Atomoxetine
- Guanfacine

I took medication as a child but have no memory of it. I'm not medicated now apart from half a gallon of CBD oil and the odd bit of cannabis. I'm aware that this may not work for everyone. I take medical cannabis because it helps with the hyperactivity that I mentioned earlier. I find that, in the evenings, the adrenaline going through my body from rushing around at work refuses to die down so I can sleep.

A quick vape is enough to help me clear my brain, clear my schedule, and lie down.

Methylphenidate is the most commonly used medicine for ADHD. It belongs to a group of stimulants. It might sound a bit odd giving stimulants to people with hyperactivity disorders, but it works by increasing activity in the brain. Our brains don't respond the same way to stimulants like caffeine or nicotine that neurotypical folk's do. This increased activity is usually in the part of the brain that controls attention and behaviour.

There are non-stimulant drugs on offer too.

Both types of medication alter the communication of messages between nerve cells, which reduces some of the issues we face as ADHD people. Some may respond to or tolerate one or the other medication.

You may be offered therapy too. I've done a lot of this at various stages and credit it with changing my life. I've struggled with more traditional forms of therapy where you just talk. I found that, ever the hyperactive, I enjoyed cognitive behaviour therapy (CBT), because it offered the chance to get proactively involved. I went to mine after a work situation turned toxic, and I was too afraid to walk out.

Here's an example of how therapy helped me through.

I have a very complex relationship with work. I completely define myself by my career and openly say I'm a workaholic. This leads me to having pretty serious Rejection Sensitivity Disorder (RSD) connected to my workplace. This is an over-simplification of this story, but it serves as an example of getting help when you need it.

I was being badly bullied by my line manager. It was a horrendous mess that resulted in my crying in the bathroom and obsessively checking sentences for mistakes. I would read my work over and over to the point of almost not wanting to submit anything for fear of my manager's scorn. I should have left months before I did, but my absolute fear of being rejected or fired kept me there. CBT helped me to understand why I was so loath to leave even when it was sucking my soul away, and then it gave me the strength to walk out. The second I gathered my things quietly, collected my coat, and walked out into the dark, I felt a sense of real freedom. Waves of relief rushed over me, and I swore I would never ever let my fear of rejection and firing get that bad again.

How Common is ADHD?

The ADHD Foundation in the UK estimates that one in five people have ADHD, autism, dyslexia, dyspraxia, dyscalculia, and/or Tourette's syndrome.[10]
I wish I'd known that as a kid growing up in rural Ireland. As I mentioned, Ireland was notoriously quiet about any form of mental health or mental differences when we were children in the 90s. We didn't talk about depression, suicide, dyslexia, or ADHD. I still know by the behaviour of the locals when a death has been a suicide because of the way it's reported. Some things never change.
There were ten kids in my primary school class. That meant, by the logic of one in five, there were two of us with extra learning needs. But we aren't alone, as diagnoses are on the rise. A study entitled *Trends in the Prevalence and Incidence of*

Attention-Deficit/Hyperactivity Disorder Among Adults and Children of Different Racial and Ethnic Groups from 2019 estimates that adult ADHD has doubled from 0.43% to 0.96% in the last decade.[11]

Welcome, my new recruits. Come on in and join the club. We've got badges.

Can You Develop Other Conditions If You Have ADHD?

I don't know about one leading to another, but you can certainly have more than one, and that's often the case. My ADHD is joined by oppositional defiance disorder, rejection sensitivity dysphoria, and chronic anxiety.

ADDitude magazine quoted a multi-author study entitled *Prevalence of Parent-Reported ADHD Diagnosis and Associated Treatment Among U.S. Children and Adolescents:*

"Nearly two thirds of children with ADHD have at least one other condition.

51.5% of children with ADHD have behavioural or conduct problems.

32.7% have anxiety problems.

16.8% have depression.

13.% have been diagnosed with autism spectrum disorder (ASD).

1.2% have Tourette's syndrome.

About 45% have a learning disorder."[12]

Is ADHD a Myth?

I hate this question.

I'm already so tired from my ADHD, so excuse me if I get fed up with the idea that I fake any of this for attention or for the fun of it. I can't change the way my brain is. While people without neurodiversity say they are accepting, they do not understand how draining it is to exist in a world not built to accommodate you.

For instance… Judge me if you will, but I remember when I was a teenager, I was really into nu-metal. It was the early 2000s, so bands like Limp Bizkit were everywhere. I was completely taken with wearing wide-legged jeans that soaked up all the water in puddles as you walked through town. Living in Ireland where it rained a lot, it meant I was constantly dragging denim around soaked up to my knees.

It was deeply uncool to admit you liked Limp Bizkit, because the mainstream kids were pretending to enjoy them. One of the other musicians, the guitarist Big Dumb Face was rumoured to be ADHD. It wasn't hard to spot that this may be the case as he was the only one out of the baggy trousers, backwards cap-wearing American guys to be in full body paint. He wore black contact lenses years before I saw anyone else do it. I took comfort in his otherness, where he stood out against the normally dressed members of the band. I took comfort in it, because I, too, elaborately dressed in black lipstick, furry leg warmers, had piercings, and carried a coffin-shaped backpack.

Years later, I was gutted to read that he told journalist Jenny Eliscu of *Rolling Stone* that he considers it a made-up condition.

"I was on a medication called Dexedrine for about six years for something that, to me, doesn't even exist called attention-deficit hyperactivity disorder—which I think is something that society made up, because not all people fit into the same educational system."[13]

I wonder if he has changed his mind since. It's not just feeling disappointed by statements like this; it sets us back when people in the public eye make statements like that, opinions that can be used against us when people want to say ADHD isn't real or that they can't give us extra help.

What is RSD?

Healthline states that rejection sensitive dysphoria "occurs when you experience an intense or overwhelming emotional sensitivity to criticism or rejection. It can be a learned emotional response, or you may be genetically predisposed to it."[14]

RSD is one of my least favourite bits of being ADHD. I realise that no one enjoys rejection, but it can break us in terms of work, relationships, and family. Those who are ADHD or autistic are particularly prone to RSD, which means extreme emotional sensitivity to being criticised or rejected, but this could be real or how it's interpreted. This is thought to be down to our difficulties with regulating our emotions and our inability to control our responses very well.

I find that RSD manifests for me as an extreme fear of abandonment, where I spend a huge amount of time attempting to pre-empt someone leaving me or firing me from a job. Often, ADHD people look for and recognise patterns in the strangest of places, as we get a dopamine rush from being the first to connect the dots. Also, our brains work differently from neurotypical people, so it makes sense that we see things in a new light. One of mine is adding up how many times someone doesn't say "I love you" of their own accord. To me, this means they're clearly not in love or feeling the same way I do. I'll always know how many times I've said "I love you" first, prompting a response from the other person. This is an imaginary rejection that I sit waiting for, and it's a sign of a low self-esteem that's exhausting. You're constantly running interactions, conversations, and encounters over in your brain, picking apart the moments of weakness that mean they'll leave you.

Yet, you may never mention this to your partner for fear of looking insane. So sit back and enjoy the absolute number this does on your mental health in that you can count on feeling depressed, anxious, terrified, and in a constant state of absolute fear that you're about to be fired or dumped at any given moment.

This can also trigger depression, social phobias, and post-traumatic stress disorder (PTSD) after a while. I have to admit that lying in wait for a job to reject me has left me completely exhausted and drained, and on occasion, I've quit before I thought they were going to fire me. Only to learn that this was all in my head after I'd left wherever I was working...

In an article on RSD and ADHD, Dr William Dodson estimates that RSD is made worse by childhood traumas. I felt plenty of abandonment and feelings of not being good enough, which was reinforced by the way my significant relationships were ended. I wasn't enough for S, so they constantly left me. I was bullied out of a friendship group as a teenager and given up for adoption as a child. In the workplace, I was surprised with firing and redundancy twice, which I internalised as me not being good enough. My self-esteem plummeted as a result, and I began to believe I was an absolute fuck-up not deserving of love or people who wanted to be around me for any length of time. This expression—fuck-up—appears on many of my teenage diaries and also in my therapy notes when I was a child. I feel sad that when I was ten, I already fully believed I was unlovable.

Post-lockdown, this heightened for me in that I became terrified of being alone again. I appreciate that no one wants to be left behind or hurt, but ADHD people have a higher chance of having RSD. It can actually feel like physical pain for us. This is potentially down to our lack of ability to regulate our emotions or read people's intentions. To counteract this, I go into a state of hypervigilance where I'm watching for signs that someone is about to leave me or doesn't love me so that I can justify not placing my trust in them or save myself from getting hurt.

In the same article on RSD, Dodson wrote, "RSD can make adults with ADHD anticipate rejection—even when it is anything but certain. This can make them vigilant about avoiding it, which can be misdiagnosed as social phobia... Rejection sensitivity is hard to tease apart. Often, people can't find the words to describe its pain. They say it's intense, awful, terrible, overwhelming. It is always triggered by the perceived or real loss of approval, love, or respect."[15]

My behaviour changes instantly when I perceive rejection as imminent. At best, I go quiet and panic. At my worst, I become defiant and badly behaved; I'll switch my phone off or spend time convincing myself that it doesn't matter if they don't love me because I don't love them either.

Sadly, the help I've seen suggested for this is medication and psychotherapy which, in today's post-lockdown, strained NHS is impossible. There's a huge waiting list for therapy, which means you can't get the help you need when you need it. Also, medication isn't for everyone, and it costs money in a cost-of-living crisis.

By now, you may have recognised some of your own behaviours or those of someone you love…or maybe you haven't. So let's get to what you came here for: sex and ADHD.

Chapter Four
The Art of Distraction

This is what happens when I try to orgasm. It's more of a pattern than I care to admit to, regardless of who it is I happen to be having sex with. I'm stretched out over the bed while lying on my front. A guy I'm seeing is having sex with me from behind while I bury my head in the black sheets. We're both naked. It's the middle of the afternoon during the global pandemic that means we're all working from home or furloughed. I've had nothing to drink, no CBD, no cannabis, no anything that could help me stop feeling like I'm feeling right now. I'm burying my head because I'm *completely* aware of everything that's happening. While the sex is consensual, the thoughts and emotions in my head are not. I haven't given them permission to take over, but that's what has happened. I'm obsessed with *everything*: the smells, noises, sounds, and beads of sweat on our bodies. All of these sensations are overwhelming—and not in a good way. I need my brain to stop. Somehow, I feel burying my head into the duvet will dislodge these emotions. The short, sharp turn of my head when I do this will hopefully break the stream of horrible thoughts bombarding me right now.

I was mid-breakup rebound from someone I had planned on proposing to. R and I had been together almost two years and had split in April 2020 following our disastrous attempt at moving in together. My breakup with R inspired this book in many ways as I realised I really didn't want to keep losing people to my ADHD. I didn't even know if ADHD had had anything to do with our breakup, but it was time to find out.

This was the first man I'd had sex with since my relationship with R broke down and took me with it. I'd done it because I couldn't stand the idea of having sex with a woman right then. I almost wanted to test myself to see what would happen. While I hadn't burst into flames at the sight of a penis, I had realised I wasn't really into it. It would, however, have seemed rude to ask him to leave. I was also aware of the way he treated me when we weren't having sex, which amounted to a form of self-harm. In that hurt state, I was more than happy to accommodate it. I was punishing myself for ruining a long-term, loving relationship with a woman I was meant to be proposing to the following year. This wasn't dating but a mild form of self-induced emotional abuse masquerading as having a good time.

And of course, my mind wasn't one to let me have a nice afternoon of sex without getting involved, especially when I wasn't into it.

"You know from this angle, he can clearly see how fat you are."

"He's not actually interested in you; he'll have sex with anyone."

"Have you ever thought that your intrusive thought process means you have OCD?"

"When are you going to sort out the cracks in that wall?"

"It smells in here."

"Your bum looks huge from that angle."

Smells and sounds filled my senses, demanding I paid attention to them. That all added up, overwhelmed me, and left me exhausted as I begged my mind to stop. I normally like to have a drink or six before I have sex, but this man didn't drink, so I was stuck being aware of everything that was happening, and I hated it. I was also bored, so my brain was hoping he hurried up so I could go back to doing something else. This is the impatient side of my ADHD brain. It's the same little frustrated voice I get when I have to sit still at the hairdressers or at meetings go on that little bit too long.

The more I tried to force my mind to be quiet, the louder it shouted and showed me images I didn't want to see and thoughts I didn't want to think. Louder and louder until it felt like I was internally screaming, because I couldn't concentrate in order to actually achieve orgasm or get any sensation from the act. My brain pushed the image of someone I disliked into my mind, and I buried my head into the bed covers again. It often shows me images of people I know or the cat in order to throw me off. I couldn't concentrate on my partner at all. The music stopped before switching to another mindless guitar track, which brought me back into the room temporarily. The guy moved me into another position, and I contemplated asking him to stop. I didn't know where I'd been those past few minutes, but it was anywhere but there.

Nothing annoys me faster than when neurotypical people pretend this happens to them too. A certain level of it does, certainly, but their lives aren't consumed by not being able to pay attention, even in the most intimate of moments. I find this particularly exhausting, because there's no way other than to fake it to get through it. So over the years, I've become a talented actor when it comes to pretending I'm enjoying sex. I don't want to draw attention to how it isn't working for me, because that would mean awkward conversations and asking people to accommodate my needs, which I'm not great at doing. So I just mimic what I think is the right thing to do is, moaning where I think I should be or adding an occasional "oh my god."

Meanwhile, my brain was filled with thoughts of R and what she could be doing right now and where she could possibly be. The frustration was palpable, and I felt like my partner had *got* to be aware of it, surely, yet he didn't seem to realise that Id shown more interest in the crack in the ceiling than I had him.

The event finished when he did and I didn't, although I'm exhausted from playing pretend.

Overwhelmed and Overtired

Like I've said, the world isn't built for neurodivergent people. From school to work, we're expected to behave like "normal folk," which is to say that we're encouraged to behave in one linear way with no exceptions. A good example of this is when I attempt to go for a drink with my friends but spend the entire night biting my tongue so as not to give them an overload of information, not talk too much, and to balance the conversation without seeming like I'm doing so. I also need to focus on what they're saying without being distracted by the overwhelming noises around me. Recently, over burgers in Bristol with my friend Scott, I could barely string a sentence together as the man at a table near me was talking too loudly. The music was also turned up to drown out the waitresses as they moved tables around. "I'm sorry," I said while miserably staring at the table, "I can't think straight." I was so disappointed in myself for not managing better.

While I'm sitting there trying to do conversation like a neurotypical, I'm expending more mental energy attempting to figure out how to do it in a way that won't irritate or annoy my friends.

Let's talk about sex and how this lack of concentration and increased exhaustion combine to make an incredibly unsexy situation.

When I interviewed a group of women about their sex lives and it came time to talk about focusing on partners, they all struggled with how their ADHD interrupted their ability to be intimate with someone.

Mandi, thirty-eight, was diagnosed later in life but connected the dots when it came to their interactions with men and how they were unable to focus. "I have difficulty focusing on my partner because my mind is always racing. I'm focused more on my inner monologue, which is quite mean. Some of the thoughts I have are focused on how inadequate I am during the experience rather than how that partner is making me feel in the moment."

I completely understand this. ADHD is so closely linked to anxiety, and a lot of us have both conditions.

"I have had one partner who could make me orgasm," Mandi said. "Even then, I would be distracted by other things. This particular partner was very good at bringing me back into the present by talking to me in a way that wasn't shameful. It allowed me to feel that what he was doing was going to get me there."

Kindness and communication are key in knowing what your ADHD partner needs to make them come. Part of this kindness and communication can help with the sense of vulnerability and exposure that goes along with being naked in bed with someone—which can be so much more intense when you're neurodivergent and juggling boundaries and emotions you can't regulate.

The cost of passing can refer to the extra tiredness and strain felt by neurodivergent folk who are expected to change their way of thinking or behaviour in order to fit neurotypical standards. For me, an example of this is feeling exhausted after forcing myself to sit still in the cinema for three hours because there are no breaks and nothing active for me to do. I come out feeling like I've been through the ringer, yet my neurotypical friends find it relaxing.

When it comes to sex, it stands to reason that if you have sex without telling your partner what works for you, then they'll automatically expect you to conform to what they like. Discussion is vital, and you won't get the extra help you need if you don't ask for it. The reverse is also true. You can't help your partner if you don't talk to them about what extra needs they may have. For instance, as part of my ADHD, I struggle with eye contact. I worry that I stare too much, I give away a lot, and I find eye contact too invasive for me. During sex, it's pretty much impossible for me, so I spend a lot of time looking anywhere but at my partner. Which can often feel a bit unnerving for someone who's attempting to connect with me.

The distractions we deal with, which we're so often told are negative, are part of who we are as ADHD people. We need to realise that the way we go about sex has to be different. We need to stop having sex like we're all the same type of person, and we need to be more vocal about our specific needs. We need partners who take that extra time, much like the above interaction Mandi had, to help us feel in the moment. This only comes with communication and an understanding of what you actually need, which can take time.

In my first relationship after writing this book, I'm still communicating what I need from my partner months into our time together. I find that there are things that I didn't know about myself until recently, and this changes with age too, so my needs are different at *cough* almost forty, compared to twenty-six. I will now talk to a partner about my ADHD before I have a relationship with them and what ADHD means for them, for me, and for us. That includes our sex life. I need to ask for more time spent on foreplay and an understanding that if I can't orgasm, they won't make me feel guilty or feel guilty themselves for it.

It's an ongoing process which takes a lot of education, understanding, and clarity.

Orgasm Pressure

I've had only three orgasms from other people in my life, despite being sexually active since I was fifteen. I didn't experience an orgasm until I was twenty-five, although I was able to get close to one by masturbating. I just couldn't figure out why they weren't happening with other people, or what I needed, or even that my ADHD was getting in the way.

In my relationship with G, we'd made a huge leap in the time we had been dating. I had followed him to Nottingham in the hope that we could start a sort of life for ourselves, and I would get a career as recession-riddled Ireland hadn't exactly been working out for me. I was staying in his cramped student flat with a horrible bed which took up the majority of the room. G was more interested in sex than I was, and that had started to cause problems. I would do anything to avoid sex with him by faking headaches, period pains, or deadlines. I had no idea why I was doing it, but the more I focused on my reading, TV, or whatever else I was doing, the less I was able to change direction to feeling up for sex.

This was the start of my guilt over my hyposexuality.

Hyposexuality is defined this way: *n. an abnormally low level of sexual behaviour. Hyposexual individuals may show no sex drive or interest in sexual activity.*

I was never diagnosed with hyposexuality but through research, I've realised it makes sense. I have always had a low sex drive bordering on non-existent. I briefly considered asexuality at one stage, but this didn't apply to me as I still experience certain feelings and had some interest in sex. However, the hyposexuality I experience forms a very distinctive pattern within my relationships.

The guilt around a lack of desire makes the situation a lot worse, but that's the natural reaction to a partner who feels cut out or isolated by a lack of sex. So, feeling guilty while in messy student accommodation wasn't where I thought

I'd experience my first orgasm, but it happened.
I gave him a hand job while he used his fingers
on me. I started to feel an intense pressure that
normally didn't happen. I don't remember if I asked
him to keep going or not, but it worked, and I felt
incredible afterwards. I passed out on his bed,
unable to move. I often wondered what worked that
time that didn't work any other time. I've come to
the conclusion that it was the physical grounding of
my touching him and focusing my attention on that
as much as I could. It kept me in the moment rather
than letting me fade away and get lost.

The useful thing here would have been to work
out what I had done that had made a difference.
However, at that stage, I still thought that I could
almost train my body into having orgasms, and once
I had one, then it would be really easy. The reality
of this was that until I took full responsibility for my
own pleasure and ADHD, I wouldn't have another
until I was thirty-two.

Another thing to note when it comes to having
sex as an ADHD person is that there's another
form of shame or guilt that we feel when it comes
to orgasm. We are constantly told that the female
orgasm is easy, achievable, and the ultimate sign
of good sex. Good sex is defined as both parties
having an orgasm at the end of the act, according
to society and women's magazines. Sex can't just be
about the intimacy or closeness to your partner but
must be about the main event and the end result.
Sex usually ends when the man comes because,
well, that's it. Whether or not the woman has come
is often an aside. As I mentioned elsewhere, orgasm
for me was beyond difficult, and in no way matched
up to those magazine headlines telling me how to

do it perfectly.

Sex with women blew my mind—it was so different. There was no end to it or the ways to have sex when the patriarchal idea of penetration is removed. By that, I mean penetration with a penis attached to a human, as I'm aware a lot of women like dildos. However, a dildo doesn't have an orgasm, roll over, and light a cigarette when done.

I worried for years that I wouldn't know what I was doing or how lesbians officially had sex. I avoided same-sex relationships and sex for years because I was so worried I would be awful at it. Eventually, I took the plunge when I dated a girl called J in Dublin. I went round to her house after my media law class, and she cooked me dinner. We watched the lesbian classic film, *But I'm a Cheerleader*, and when we finally did have sex, I was amazed at how easy it was. Was this really what I had been worrying about for so long? I took the Luas (tram) back into the city centre the next morning feeling like everyone knew what I'd been doing that night.

When it came to having sex with women, the same problems were still there though. I couldn't come. I couldn't switch off or enjoy myself, because my ADHD was still a problem. However, I did find that my anxiety around having sex with women lessened a lot after that night, and I began to relax a bit more around the idea of coming out as LGBT+, although it would be years before that happened.

I found the same pressure remained around the idea of orgasms. It was just as expected when I had sex with women as it had been with men, although women were more open to the idea of spending time trying to figure out what worked instead of jumping straight to penetrative sex. I found it far more enjoyable having sex with women in that respect, because it felt more caring, but it wasn't until I had long-term relationships that I was able to vocalise my lack of concentration and issues around orgasms.

Guilt, shame, distraction, and exhaustion don't make for a sexy experience. It also made me feel like my mind was broken. I worked in a high street sex shop for two years where innuendo, advertising, and marketing told me with a cheeky wink that the BIG O was something that could be easily achieved if I bought the right thing, had the right man, or experimented the right way. I couldn't just have sex and expect that to be enough for my body; I had to have all the bells and whistles that money could buy.

While working in that sex shop, I purchased one of every toy ever made in a bid to exhaust not only my staff discount but to find the mythical toy that the marketing promised would cure everything. The marketing, the adverts, and all of the sex chat was overwhelmingly heterosexual. There were hundreds of vibrator styles in the store but only one strap-on, which had little white daises on it. There were rows of big, veiny plastic penises to choose from. As a former smut seller, I'm delighted now to see how far the sex industry has come, with its space age dildos that don't look anything like the fake dicks of almost twenty years ago.

But at that time, we were far from apps and iPhone-assisted sex toys. I spent every day for two years surrounded by basic lubes, chains, and dildos that looked like penises. My conversations about sex became easy, because I would talk to customers casually as if I was discussing the weather. "If it's a nine-inch realistic dildo you want, then you'll need a lube with that," was as simple as, "It's a nice day, isn't it? Grand stretch in the evenings." I was also surrounded by the marketing message that all the women out there, according to my job and *Cosmopolitan*, were having sex and coming all over the place. I feel a sadness for that twenty-year-old me, selling vibrators and lube for a hundred quid in boom time Ireland where I lied and said that good sex was guaranteed because of the price. The whole time, my ADHD self was exhausted by the emotions and thought of having sex.

The Science, the Silence, and How it Lets Us All Down

We're let down by studies that ignore women and queer people. Diagnoses favour men, as do studies and books. There is less research when it comes to queer people and communities, and even less when it comes to women who are neurodivergent as opposed to neurotypical. Annoying, given that there is a real need for someone to actually study what goes on.

Research on how women orgasm in *The Journal of Sex and Marital Therapy*, published in 2017, revealed that nearly 37% of women needed clitoral stimulation to come, and another 36% said that while they didn't require clitoral stimulation to orgasm, it did enhance the experience. 18% of respondents said vaginal penetration alone was sufficient for orgasm, and 9% reported that they didn't have orgasms during intercourse, or achieved orgasm in other ways, such as oral sex.[16] The study surveyed 1055 women between the ages of eighteen and ninety-four and asked women a series of questions about how they like to be touched.

This study focuses on orgasm, so neurodivergent people appear not to be mentioned despite how many of those involved must have been neurodivergent. It also doesn't seem to clarify if transgender or non-binary people are considered, as some may have the same body parts that are being discussed here. It's not the focus of most studies like this, so it gets glossed over despite it having a potential effect on the results.

When I switched the focus to ADHD people, I found a Dutch study conducted in a clinic in 2017 (why was everyone researching orgasms in 2017?). It found that of 136 ADHD-diagnosed adults, there was a high percentage of sexual dysfunction, with 39% of the men and 43% of women reporting signs. They were given two questionnaires about sexual dysfunction and sexual disorders to fill in. The instances of sexual disorders dropped in comparison to dysfunction with 17% of men and just 5% of women.

The authors concluded that "sexual dysfunctions and other sexual disorders are highly prevalent in adults with ADHD. Screening for sexual disorders should be therefore standard procedure during diagnostic assessment."[17]

Despite having ADHD-related sexual dysfunction, I do love sex. I love the grossness of it, the sweat, the smell, the feeling of it, the intimacy, and even those weird, sweaty fart noises your bodies make together. ADHD is unique to each person, which is what makes it so difficult to say how it presents. My traits can be different to someone else's or different to my partner's, making it difficult to say there's any one solution. Orgasms are the same: unique in what works for each person. Some ADHD people have hyposexuality or some may have hypersexuality. Neither is more or less "standard ADHD" than the other.

Finding Your Niche

Achieving orgasm isn't a case of finding my thing when it comes to sex. Neurotypical society is obsessed with the idea of being able to provide solutions for neurodiverse folk rather than just admitting that they could change the way society behaves, even just a little, to accommodate those who don't fit a typical pattern. I can't tell you how many times someone has told me to get a day planner as if it will magically improve my life. Not that it would be useful for sex and orgasms. Or maybe they think it would help that too. I don't know.

The assumption is that neurotypical sex isn't working for you because you're not working hard enough for it. I don't need to find my thing as I went to art college for five years and spent a vast amount of time exploring my sexual side in all kinds of ways: in threesomes, golden showers, fingering men, BDSM, etc. The list went on and on before I honed it down to the things I really like, but from 2004 to 2008, there was a chance I would literally get involved in anything just to see what I thought of it. Whatever else would you be doing in art college? Actually creating art?

Telling ADHD folk that they just need to find out what they're into is a bit offensive. It is, to me at least, another way of saying, "Urgh, just conform already." As if the day planner or figuring out I like fisting are going to make me any less ADHD or make me come instantly. While there are some who figure out that they like wearing PVC gimp masks, I don't think it's going to make you any less ADHD on a day-to-day basis. But it might help you a bit in the bedroom.

I worked hard to find this magical cure that the neurotypical folk spoke of. The only sex that seems to work for me is when I trust the other person, when they have patience, and kindness, and more importantly, they take my neurodiversity into account. This means listening to me, understanding my boundaries, bringing me back into the room, and grounding me into my own body. This took time to understand, and it doesn't work every time. I'm thirty-five, and I've had three accidental orgasms with other people. Nothing about that qualifies me to write a sex book, but here we are.

So what happens when the lack of sex has reached a crisis point in a relationship? In my case, I medicated myself, and I medicated hard.

Self-medication and the Culture of Craic

This is going to be a hard topic for me to write about. While I'm not an alcoholic, I do consider my drinking to be problematic at times. I like to add the "but I don't" caveat to everything which goes as follows: "Sure I like six pints of cider on a Wednesday night the same as the next person, BUT I DON'T drink in the morning."

I consider a lot of Irish people to have an issue with drinking, which is why reading this section will be hard for a lot of people. We've all been brought up in the same culture, the culture of craic.

In her book, *Good Morning, Destroyer of Men's Souls*, Nina Renata Aron describes something called "alcoholism-light," which I believe a lot of us who engage in craic culture would possibly recognise. "I had come to see light alcoholism as normal human behaviour, and compared with other drugs, alcohol certainly wasn't the worst thing to be hooked on… These glasses, here on this bar, catching the twinkling light, these were just drinks! They were no big deal."[18]

A great deal of learning to drink in Ireland is learning to look the other way. You learn to ignore alcoholism or problem drinking because it's jokingly referred to as "being fond of the drink" rather than any words that suggest a person is suffering. You learn to accept that hangovers, black-outs, fights, and falls are part of a normal night out. It happens to everyone, you say as you patch up a friend's knees after they fall, or you're stuck on the couch wasting a day with a hangover so bad you can't move. You don't understand or never learn to recognise when to call time on a session. Where's the fun in an early night or just one pint?

My drinking falls into a pattern that I think a lot of people will recognise as part of this culture. We value drink more than we should. The ability to hold your drink is a skill rather than a worrying tolerance, and we're known all over the world for our ability to have a good time. I too, am known for having a good time, and I'm the one people call for a few drinks or a night out. "Arrah, just the one so," I say confidently, reaching for my third large white wine on a Wednesday night. I don't appear to have an off switch when it comes to drinking.

The lack of an off switch came in handy when

I started drinking to cover the guilt I felt around avoiding sex. I would orchestrate a night out where I could hide behind too many pints to avoid getting intimate when we got home. As my tolerance grew, I needed more pints to get to the stage where I could comfortably lie about being drunk as an excuse.

I've loved drinking since I started in my twenties. I didn't start young like a lot of my friends who started "bushing" as teenagers. Bushing was the art of taking small vodka bottles (naggins) or cans of sweet and cheap cider into fields because you couldn't do it at home. I started in art college by drinking a ton of disgusting drinks I now wouldn't touch. My favourite was to mix a pint of neon-green fat frog, which was an orange Bacardi Breezer, a Smirnoff Ice, and a blue Wicked. It was rumoured to get you absolutely pissed but the truth was, it gave you a huge high from the sugar and an even bigger crash afterwards. I loved the craic of drinking, because everything blurred, so the noises and sensitivity I was bombarded with quietened down considerably, while also giving me the confidence to fuel my adventures. In her memoir, *Blackout*, Sarah Hepola wrote, "I wanted my own stories, and I understood drinking to be the gasoline of adventure. The best evenings were the ones you might regret."[19]

Regrets? I've had a few…

While I claim to drink less problematically than I did in my twenties, I simply do it differently now. In my twenties, a cheap bottle of whatever was on offer and guaranteed to get us messed up would do the trick. In my thirties, the quality and price tag of wine has increased, and the drinking is less nightclubbing and more PJs, scruffy topknot, and in bed by eleven p.m. Lockdown life certainly saw the inclusion of evening wines more often than I cared to admit. That said, there are still times where I wake up and worry… Do I need to call someone?

Alcohol abuse is something I have to watch out for. I come from a biological line of alcoholic people, so if you believe in hereditary behaviours, then I could be in trouble down the line. It's also something we, as ADHD people, have to watch out for, because it can be a medication replacement in the best and worst way. I spoke about the intrusive thoughts I have on a daily basis and how overwhelming they can be. How I sat in the restaurant with my friend Scott and felt genuinely miserable that I could barely speak to him because of the distractions. True to form as the eternal party person, I ordered a large white wine despite his plain Coke and got mildly buzzed in the hope it would shut the noise down. Alcohol offers us a way out of this. It gives relief when it forces those emotions, noises, distractions, and behaviours to silence.

Substance Abuse Disorder (SUD) statistics are particularly sobering amongst ADHD people. Studies suggest that 25 to 40% of adults with SUD are also ADHD.[20] That's not a small percentage. Also, ADHD people are 1.5 times more likely to develop substance abuse disorders to substances such as nicotine, alcohol, cannabis, or cocaine.[21] Alcohol abuse can worsen some of our symptoms, including issues with cognition difficulties, decision-making, memory, and speech.

At some stage as we grow older, we have to admit to ourselves, however hard it is, that the party is over. This can be a difficult issue for me, because as my friends deal with grown-up things, I'm the one they call when they want to escape the baby/wife/job/reality for a bit. As someone who doesn't date men, I'm safe to let husbands or men folk out with and in turn, they know I'll always be up for a pint or sixteen. When they go home mildly buzzed to my staggered walk, they don't contact me for weeks until they fancy a flutter around town. Then my phone blows up again with calls or texts to "catch up" which is code for, let's go out. It's hard not to feel resentful of this role but I keep casting myself in it.

This can include making it easier for someone to leave me by casting myself in roles like this. I'm less of a person, more of an experience, so I'm easier to leave so people feel less conflicted about why they no longer want to see me. "Ah, it's a Wednesday, and I don't want to get wrecked," they think most weeks when it crosses their mind that they haven't called me in a while. It's a paradox. I don't want them to leave me, but I also don't want to make it hard for them to leave me if they really don't want to be around me. This Mad Hatter kind of logic doesn't make for an easy stroll through life.

Revisiting the book, *Good Morning, Destroyer of Men's Souls*, Nina Renata Aron writes about having a circle of heavy drinkers. There was a definite connection for me in the creative, left-brain thinkers that I was hanging out with at the time. The art college I went to was a breeding ground for the tortured artist, where drugs and heavy drinking was part of the stereotype in action. It wasn't just that, but despite our creativity, there were no jobs available in Ireland for arty folk. So we drank to get through the day jobs we worked instead of the careers we were sold a notion of when we started college. This is where I developed habits and patterns that surround my drinking even to this day, where it crossed over into problematic. I was often the instigator of the madness and the one pushing my friends into yet another wine. While my friends were out for a good time, I was self-medicating my exhaustion at trying to get my ADHD brain to cooperate and let me get on with work and life. The more I drank, the less sharp my brain got, so I didn't notice every last sound, and I was happier to just sit back and relax.

Aron wrote, "Once I left home, I entered a long period of heavy drinking and every single one of my friends was the same. They were writers and musicians who drank in torment and ecstasy and tried to create meaningful works of art. They worked in restaurants and bars and took shots behind the counter. Or they worked in the dark administrative corners of non-profits or under fluorescent lights in cubicles and drank to blow off steam. We drank to go out, to be out, to be seen, to kill time and we drank to fuck. We drank to find the nerve to do any of the things we wanted to, and we drank to dull the disappointment of doing those things, of realising that so many of life's imagined high points were in fact, mediocre."[22]

I remember those years with friends who had yet to be married, have children, or be consumed with trips to B&Q on the weekend. We were all on a level, celebrating life together and raising glasses with third, fourth, and fifth pints in them. Somehow, over the years, this flow of hard drinking had slowed to a trickle, and it was only me left standing.

One time, over a cold pint in the Bodega bar that I frequented for cheap pints, I had just finished telling the story of my last first date to a female friend. She'd left her newborn baby and gorgeous husband for the night to go out with her best single friend. I had just finished the story, gesturing with a flourish of my drink hand. "And that's when she put me in a cab at two in the morning and never called again!" I screamed with laughter.

She looked at me and my eyeliner artfully smudged around my slightly red eyes and said with deep pity, "Man, I am so grateful not to be single anymore."

I have long worried that my love of a good time combined with my neurodivergence has doomed me to a lonely single life. Her comment hit hard, so I did what came naturally to me, I ordered another pint and commenced getting wasted mid-week as I always did.

I have, on occasion, walked a fine line between too drunk to continue and too drunk for true consent. I am choosing not to think about this because I can't. I took fine line drinking to the limit where I realised I was choosing to get that little bit too drunk in order to avoid sex. I was getting so wasted there was no way I could have sex. Mentally, I wouldn't admit this to myself, but in practice, that's what was happening.

One example of this still haunts me frequently.

I was in Berlin for New Year's Eve, and I was in love, sort of. I was with my girlfriend, R, and we had reached the tail end of our relationship but had yet to realise that's where we were. I'd put considerable time into my outfit, and I sat cross-legged on the floor surrounded by makeup, which I was painting on my face. I loved that part of the night where it's all DJing your favourite tunes, doing a proper paint from scratch using all the products I didn't have time for on my daily makeup routine and topping up glasses frequently. R and I had two bottles of Prosecco, and we were, before we even went out, drunk. We had been tipping away at wine all day on our walks around the city, so in truth, neither of us knew how much we'd had. We left down the rickety staircase in a blaze of glitter and heels before the freezing cold German air shocked some life into us. Soakage dinner didn't happen as we missed our booking for pre-drinking carbohydrates. We stopped for sushi at a cheap café, which turned out to be a rookie mistake as sushi is terrible soakage for a heavy night. We chased down sashimi slices with warm wine. I was enjoying the buzz of a new city. I lived for the dopamine hit that came with finding strange and unusual bars. I loved the challenge of finding a truly unique pub in an alleyway or a hidden space.

I'd been drinking not just because I like it but also because I knew R would want to have sex with me when we got home. I loved her but I was struggling emotionally, and I didn't know about my hyposexuality or lack of sex drive at that stage. I just knew what I felt, although I didn't go about analysing it. I wanted to be with her, love her, hold her and be by her side, but I couldn't bring myself to have sex with her because of the way my mind works. And the more I worried about it, the worse it got. I hated myself for it and felt a deep shame and guilt for what I knew she was feeling because of me. I'd avoided talking to her outside of an argument, so I chose to get drunk instead, hoping it might

make me want to have sex later on. Although I
suspected this wasn't the case, so dread was slowly
entering the evening, and I reminded myself we
hadn't had sex in weeks. Our last sex had been on
another holiday on the first night. We spent the rest
of the holiday arguing about why we had only had
sex once.

Several Berlin bars later, after warm wine in
plastic cups and a packed dive bar where a woman
made a sandwich on the table beside us, complete
with mayonnaise from a jar, we staggered home. I
didn't remember the walk home at all, which scared
me, but we made it. We kissed in the terrifyingly
rickety elevator and took a selfie together, which
reminded me the next day that we got home
safely. We went to bed and when we were in our
underwear kissing, a wave of exhaustion came
over me. It's the sort of tiredness that comes when
you know you're about to black out. I could either
surrender gracefully or embarrass myself later on.

I had to tell her, so I did.

"Hey, I need to stop," I slurred apologetically.
"I'm too drunk. I need to sleep." I shook the loose
glitter out of my hair while she looked at me.

She started to kiss my neck and said, "I'd like to
continue, please."

I cringe as I remember this. We both knew this
was where consent had been withdrawn, so she
stopped. I sat on the bed, and I was aware for
the first time that this behaviour wasn't working
anymore. I couldn't keep drinking in the hopes of
changing things. We sat on the bed beside each
other, and another first time thought ran through
my head. I didn't think we were going to make it
through the year together. We were a million miles

apart in that exact second despite almost touching physically. This was the woman I'd asked to move in with me, who I planned on proposing to, but my hyposexuality was threatening to destroy us. But I didn't have the words yet for this thing that happens to me sexually, and so it continued to create a path of destruction.

I stood on unsteady feet and removed my earrings. "It's not you...." I couldn't even look at her. I knew she was hurt and disappointed. Excuses are useless in this situation when you know you've hurt someone you love like that. I should have *wanted* to have sex with her. After all, we were in love, and it was a special occasion, right? Our Airbnb host had left us a mini red wine in the bedroom with two glasses for this exact reason. We were expected to have sex, not an early night. We silently went to bed, and it was never mentioned again.

It was just one more night to add to the growing list of times I'd caused that fight. No matter what city we had it in, the crux of it remained the same.

It breaks my heart that I've spent so much time with this pattern that I know it by heart. Melissa Orlov and Nancie Kohlenberger in their book, *The Couple's Guide to Thriving with ADHD*, break my heart further by saying, "ADHD partners who have learned to live with the impact of their ADHD symptoms are often oblivious to the very real emotional problems and stress their symptoms encourage in their partners."[23] I see this stress and heartbreak all over my relationship with R.

There is a higher percentage of ADHD people suffering from alcohol issues and dependency, along with drug abuse. I'm not alone in my desire to escape the emotions, guilt, shame, and lack of understanding I live with on a daily basis. Chemical dependency is a crutch many of us lean on, and it chills me.

Frank South, when writing for the ADHD positive website, *ADDitude*, talks about his drinking in terms of his ADHD, and it makes for uncomfortable reading. "I think everyone sometimes has critical and defensive voices chattering away in their heads. But our ADHD often increases, accentuates, and amplifies that noise into an anxiety-ridden, confusing, dark storm, and a couple of stiff drinks at first seems to work miracles; the volume shuts down, you're no longer anxious, and what seemed impossible to accomplish suddenly seems eminently doable. That's what's sneaky about drinking; sometimes it helps in the short run. It does turn off the voices, takes the self-criticism and obsession with all the things you could have done better down a notch, and comforts you by saying, "Hey, no worries, you'll do better tomorrow. Look at all the great ideas you're having—you're on a roll now, see?"[24] I think an ADHD brain especially craves this kind of comfort and semblance of peace. And an ADHD alcoholic's brain will full-on fight to the death to keep it."

I don't have an alcoholic's brain, do I? I would be lying if I said that my drinking hasn't been problematic. It feeds into the risk-taking factor too. Alcohol lowers the inhibitions, which means I'm leaving myself open to the possibility of risky sex, dangerous situations, and bad partners. Adding alcohol into the mix seems like an even worse situation.

Bryony Gordon's book *Mad Girl* is about her struggle with OCD that really hit home. In one chapter, she talks about how she came to realise she was doing a bit too much cocaine to quiet the feelings of OCD. "On cocaine, I am not me. I am a much better version of me. I am me but sexier, spunkier, sassier. I am me without the OCD, me without the fear. All the stuff that mattered a moment before I snorted the line simply ceases to exist. Snifffff. Ping! Cocaine is what I use to quieten my OCD—later, I learn that it is not uncommon for these to go side by side—and it is what I use to pretend to everyone that I am happy."[25]

In recent times, having sex sober has been weirdly liberating while incredibly frustrating at the same time. For the first few times, although I wasn't going to orgasm, I did feel satisfaction of not being black-out drunk, and there was a smugness to having made it. I was proud of myself for being able to make a conscious, liberated, and sober decision. A voice at the back of my head recognises that I shouldn't feel pride at not drinking. To have this feeling suggests that I know my drinking is more problematic than I admit to. I am practicing the Irish ritual of looking the other way.

Sarah Hepola's wonderful memoir of giving up drinking contains her thoughts on drunken sex. In the book, she writes, "I always thought good sex without alcohol would be sharp with detail, saturated with colour, but instead it was more like a four p.m. sun flare. Pleasure shuts down the recorder in the brain. The flood of serotonin and dopamine creates a white-hot burst of ecstasy. For decades, I drank myself to reach that place of oblivion. Why hadn't I known? The oblivion could come to me."[26]

I have a strong pattern of hyperactivity in the

early days of relationships that creates an addictive rush. ADHD creates a desperate need for extra dopamine, so falling in love gives us that glorious hit we crave. Not only that but we don't regulate our emotions easily, so we feel everything so much more intensely. I'm all over a person when we first start dating in an intense way which can be really flattering to someone. I'm not a crazy stalker, I should add, in that I obviously don't do anything scary or break the law when it comes to my intense feelings. I find myself constantly texting, chatting, mentioning, and chasing a person. It must feel incredibly cruel when this hyperactive streak finishes, and I lose interest. It doesn't mean I stop loving them, but that intensity is gone. I get that neurotypical people do this too, and it's often described as a love rush, but it's not as intense as neurodiverse folk find it to be. The neglect and loneliness I put R through, when all I should have had done is talk to her, will haunt me whenever I think about our relationship which is, post-breakup, all the damn time.

The sex drive fades away with the hyperfocus on that person. I wish I had realised it sooner and done something about it. Instead, "We need to talk" became a regular occurrence in my relationship with R, and it went around in circles. R would beg to know what she was doing wrong, what was going on with me, and what she could do. I simply didn't know. I wouldn't do anything about it, therefore breaking her heart repeatedly in the process. Guilt isn't an aphrodisiac.

Guilt and Avoidance

I was lying in bed in R's house, wrapped in the duvet and staring at the ceiling. I'd just kissed R good night and was quietly basking in the relief that came when she didn't want to have sex. I hadn't had to come up with a collection of excuses that sounded pathetically like the bullshit they are.

The circle of shame and guilt never goes away. I'm relieved whenever I crawl into bed and my partner wants to sleep without looking for sex. I can relax and scroll through my phone until I fall asleep. But I knew that something wasn't right, and R wasn't happy. The issue of sex hung over our heads like the invisible giraffe in the room that no one mentions. Eventually, I realised R had fallen asleep, but my anxiety levels were making it hard for me to switch off.

Sari Solden and Michelle Frank talk a lot of sense in their book, *A Radical Guide for Women with ADHD*. "You may find you shrink back from closeness with friends and extended family because you feel misunderstood or afraid that you have disappointed others due to inconsistency in contact. The anxiety and avoidance that typically follow can take things to a higher level of interpersonal gridlock or isolation. You might find yourself distancing from or even actively avoiding people you once enjoyed because of this rising anxiety and shame."[27]

I don't feel this just applies to people but also to actions. I felt I'd disappointed R with my lack of wanting to have sex. The more I knew she felt let down, the more I felt I should have sex just to prove that I loved her. That created a triangle of guilt, anxiety, and shame. I noted I was actively avoiding sex by faking headaches, stress, or just saying "Not tonight" when in reality, it's every night.

Solden and Frank suggest reaching out to people even if you're avoiding them. In a sex sense, I feel this should mean having that discussion about how your sex is affected by your ADHD. "It may mean harnessing the courage to do the opposite of your habitual pull to hide, pretend, or isolate. You deserve to have connection even though you have challenges that might be difficult for some to understand. You also have the right to be treated with respect in the face of those moments."[28]

It is important to note as well that some ADHD medication may affect your sex drive. Symptoms of depression and anxiety, which neurodivergent folk have in greater numbers than neurotypical folk, can also impact sex lives. I have chronic anxiety which manifests in a number of ways, but one way it interferes with me is to make my sex drive even more non-existent. So it's not always hyposexuality but could be a result of a number of factors. What's important is that you do the work to figure out the factors at work in your own neurodivergent universe. One way of doing that is through research or reaching out to professional people who work with neurodiverse folk on education and also by being organised, among many other things.

When speaking again to Anastasia, an ADHD life coach, she stressed the importance of knowing your own brand of ADHD. "The world is set up a certain way, and it's not that you can't navigate it, but depending on your brand of ADHD, then the impairments may be specific to you. It's super important for people to know how ADHD shows up in them. A lot of the work I do is because there is still a stigma attached to it and a stereotype of little boys jumping off chairs, which doesn't really fit a lot of ADHD people, so you need to figure out how it looks for you."

I recognise a lot of my traits now because of the help I've gotten in the past year. The pandemic has been many things, mostly negative, but I have to admit that I've learned an awful lot because I've had nothing better to do with my time. I've also gotten really good at accessorising sweatpants, but this isn't the time for that.

Finding Help

A lot of self-help books talk about the "connection" with your partners. Sex creates intimacy with the other person, and if you're not having sex, that can be difficult but not impossible to maintain.

The self-help books suggested I find ways to connect to my partner while offering helpful things like running a 10k race together. While I won't be doing that any time soon, there is something to this idea of connection. I spent so much time burying my head in the sand when it came to R, pretending it was fine, that I ignored her attempts (and made none myself) to do massages, bath nights, or date nights. I lost out as a result.

So what can neurotypical people do in this situation? It's very tempting to say, "Be supportive," but it's not that simple. I imagine the answer lies in communication and in that connection idea. Becoming aware of how your ADHD could or can affect you is a good part of the battle and communicating this to your partners is essential, as is being able to recognise bad patterns of hyper- or hyposexuality. When it comes to the drinking I've mentioned, it's important to recognise that before it becomes dangerous. I'm working hard to cut mine down by reducing consumption and replacing it with something else every day. As part of my lockdown life, I decided to stop drinking during the week and only allow alcohol at the weekends. I started this unofficially for three weeks before I told anyone what I was doing. I expected people to be a bit sceptical but in fact, they were quite supportive, which told me that my family and friends may have been worried about my tolerance levels for a while. Probably due to my ODD, they had hesitated to talk to me about it. I shouldn't be able to comfortably drink two bottles of wine in a night.

Neurotypical people sometimes enjoy volunteering a way for me to control my ADHD that suggests they don't understand their privilege of living in a world that is built to accommodate their neurotype. They often don't understand how exhausting it is to be different because they haven't ever experienced having a brain that functions differently. They offer pseudo-empathy where in shrieking voices they go, "OMG, I can't concentrate. Maybe I have ADHD too!" Hands up if you have ever nearly smacked someone for saying that to your face. I know I have. Think about how casually people say, "I'm practically OCD about the cleaning," or "I'm obsessed with that band." In truth, these people can usually break those behaviours easily, because their brain allows them to. They haven't been reduced to tears because they're distressed by their own behaviour and lack of ability to change it.

Social media has offered me a world of support in recent years, where I can join groups for everything from knitting to obscure, dank memes. I find that it has offered me a chance to speak to neurodiverse people in a way I felt cut off from before. I joined so many ADHD groups that my Facebook news feed is alive with the sound of neurodivergent folk discussing their lives, concentration techniques, and that weird thing they like to do in bed.

Interviewing Shar was a revelation, as it felt so lovely to speak to another queer ADHD person. "My partner and my housemates have realised over the past year that we are all neurodiverse. It's why we clicked together so well. I've been very blessed and lucky with that sort of environment. I haven't gotten into it with my family; I kind of don't want to."

Shar has a combination of close friends but also social media-based support which has been so important to them. "I'm in a neuroqueer group online where there are, like, a hundred of us. I love neuroqueer so much as it makes me so happy. It's a space where we can talk about issues or just fun stuff. It can be a warning to each other about shitty doctors or lamenting about a crap experience. We all have each other's backs, because the pool of services you can access in Ireland is so tiny. It's nice to have a space where people are looking out for one another."

I mentioned that I felt there was a gap between online support from peers and professionals. They agree. "It can be desperate if you don't find those support groups, as you're just adrift. Sometimes you can accidentally end up in parents of ADHD children spaces where it's like nope, nope, nope."

Turning Over a New Leaf

One group made me sit up and pound the join button extra quickly. An ADHD and medical cannabis group on Facebook with over 14,000 members of all genders. I am currently a cannabis and CBD journalist with a magazine, so this caught my attention. I haven't smoked weed in six years, but I believe strongly in cannabis as medicine and think it's about time we had dispensaries for people to access this kind of help.

I started to research the effects of cannabis on ADHD, in particular for hyperactivity and hyperfocus. While my group discussion appeared to suggest that smoking cannabis had helped with their ADHD, it wasn't until 2020 that some studies appeared to suggest this may actually be the case. A study in a medical journal reported that a study of CBN on ADHD patients may have produced results. CBN is produced when the THC of a cannabis plant dries out. It was originally considered a waste product but is now being added to products in states where it is legal. It's illegal in the UK and Ireland, as cannabis generally is.

The study included fifty-nine diagnosed adults who were enrolled in a medical cannabis program, and they were divided into two groups on different doses. The group with the higher intake of cannabis (four to twelve times a day) self-reported a higher occurrence of reducing their ADHD medication as a result of their CBN intake. Those on the lower dose (up to three times a day) recorded less anxiety.[29] This is a pretty small-scale study, however, it's a positive sign that it even took place.

I turned to the ADHD/cannabis group to ask the

people there how cannabis affected their sex life?

Emily, twenty-four, from the UK said, "I am a regular smoker of cannabis, especially before sex. I find certain strains help me focus and really turn me on. For me, high sex is the best sex. Smoking relaxes me, which allows me to enjoy the sex more. I try to use it every time. It makes the experience much more enjoyable. I'm able to quiet down the noisy part of my brain and get lost in the passion of the moment. Big fan of the pre-sex smoke sesh."

This was a common answer among the women from the focus group. Alison, thirty, agreed. "I use cannabis all day, every day including before and after sex. It does help me focus and helps me feel more intensely. I find it helps me slip into the place of letting go of any tension, releasing your mind to your body for an hour, and finally having your mind be silent and feeling your body come alive."

So with that in mind, I lit up and prepared to try it. After all, if it worked, it could help me *without* the side effects that some drugs can have which might put you off sex, like anti-depressants or ADHD medications.

At the time that I made the decision to try this, I'd become very single. I found myself striking out on Tinder, having bad dates, and even having to stop the sex I was having as I realised the person was fundamentally horrendous as a human. I turned to a mate to ask them to have sex with me (as we had in the past) just as lockdown kicked in and we were banned from seeing each other. I also embarked on a text-only relationship with a policewoman in another city who I never met due to restrictions. By the time the restrictions ended, she had disappeared. The actual threat of meeting me after so long behind closed doors and cold phone screens proved too much. If I didn't hate the police before, I certainly did now.

The experiment wasn't going well so far.

Where to smoke was another issue. I had just bought my lovely new home, in which I didn't want to smoke for fear of never getting the smell out. I couldn't roll a joint because I have a strict no tobacco policy after smoking for almost ten years. I was stuck smoking in my small backyard, crouched down behind a wall. Next door's little girl often liked to stand at the window where she could see into my garden. Ordinarily, that was fine because I was usually gardening or doing some other non-illegal activity, but I really didn't want her exposed to my taking a hit. I didn't need her parents calling the police either. So, I crouched down to smoke a small bit of greenery then heard the many pops of my thirty-five-year-old knees as I got up. I was far too aware that I never used to make so much sound when I crouched down in my twenties.

The smoke hit my throat hard, leaving a burning feeling that made me cough. I wasn't a seasoned drug-taker anymore. I went back inside and decided to masturbate after I'd smoked. I had a free house but rather than feeling like masturbating, I was ultra-focused and rushed around doing housework. I thought a bit of cannabis would relax me, but it hit me right at a moment of intense hyperfocus so, much like alcohol but not as dangerous, it allowed me to dull the voices and get work done. I knew I was high when my mother called, and I struggled to make sense. I was extremely paranoid that she sensed I was high, when in reality, she simply thought I'd had a drink or two after a long day.

Eventually, I learned that masturbation isn't helped or hindered by the cannabis. I feel the same level of concentration that I normally experience when trying to masturbate, as I watch my usual porn and use my favourite purple vibrator. I'm sad that it hasn't had a huge effect in the way I hoped. What I do find is that the time to relax afterwards is better. The noises in my head disappear, and I'm blissfully curled up in bed focused on TV. I find my attention is just enough so I can watch the show, and I'm even ignoring my phone instead of mindlessly swiping through Instagram.

It feels wonderful to just be there. I feel lucky and happy to be looking after myself. I'm learning what works for me, what doesn't, and what I can say to other people about these things, which might help them in the long run.

Chapter Five
Hyperfocus, Dopamine Rushes, and Obsessive Crushes... Oh My!

"People who have the predominately hyperactive/ impulsive form of ADHD struggle a great deal with hyperactivity. They too struggle with inattentive traits, but their main challenges are related to hyperarousal and trouble 'putting on the brakes.' People with this subtype have difficulty sitting still, waiting in line, and holding back impulses to act or speak. They are fidgety and feel a constant need to be 'on the go' or have an inner sense of restlessness. They struggle with impulsivity and tend to have experienced a lot of negative consequences from uninhibited behaviours, hasty comments, and rash decision-making."[30]

YES. I thought to myself. Finally. Yes.

This quote is from the first book I've ever seen that is dedicated solely to women with ADHD. *A Radical Guide to Women with ADHD: Embrace Neuro-Diversity, Live Boldly and Break Through Barriers* by Sari Solden and Michelle Frank. It's also worth noting that this is one of the few books I have seen to mention transgender and non-binary folk too.

The ADHD Institute reckon that girls have the quieter form of ADHD, which means we are silent, and society likes it to remain that way. "Some studies have indicated that girls with ADHD may be up to twice as likely as boys to have the inattentive type of ADHD and may suffer more from internalising symptoms and inattention, in contrast with the hyperactive and aggressive symptoms shown by boys."[31] This is the very simplified version of gender, which all ADHD research seems to be concerned with. I'm either an aggressive boy or a dreamy girl and never a confused non-binary person looking for representation. All of these studies slide everyone into two genders. It's not that simple—gender is far more complex than we give it credit for.

I realised I was non-binary when neither the description of feminine nor masculine worked for me. In all honesty, I'm not even sure non-binary describes the relationship I have with my own gender, but right now, it's the only description I have. While non-binary and transgender people have been around forever, these terms are becoming so much more well-known, so who knows what terminology we'll have ten years from now.

Although I define as queer now, I've dated neurodivergent men, transgender, intersex people, and women, some of whom have had very different ADHD behaviours to mine. I think you can be the quiet type (inattentive) or the other type (hyperactive) or, as I describe myself, a fecking curious mix of both, regardless of what gender you are.

As I start to write this chapter, I'm quietly confident that this is going to be the one I have least in common with, so therefore, it will be the one I will struggle with the most. I suffer predominately from the inattentive version of ADHD, according to my mother, which means I'm often daydreaming, disorganised, and constantly struggling to sit still. I both agree and disagree with this; I do have a hyperactive side which means I'm constantly working at warp speed, but I strongly identify with the combination of the two. I wonder what it would be like to be reassessed. I'd be curious to see what new research and understanding of ADHD would make to *my* understanding of my traits. It's been twenty-four years since my diagnosis, so surely something has changed. I can hope, right?

Going back to my glossy new book (Solden and Frank, 2019), the writers explain that people can have both. "People with the combined presentation of ADHD have aspects of both the inattentive and hyperactive/impulsive presentations. Women with combined presentation often describe experiences similar to those with the inattentive presentation along with being overly talkative, prone to interrupting conversations, making impulsive decisions, and physical or mental hyperactivity."[32]

The opposite of hyposexuality should be hypersexuality. However, as I discovered while writing this, hypersexuality can also be used to describe extreme sexual behaviours like sex addition, compulsive porn watching, and problematic masturbating. These are behaviours that ADHD can mix with but may not cause. Not everyone with ADHD is a chronic masturbator or porn addict. I feel calling a high sex drive *hypersexuality* is a bit unfair. Here, I'm focusing on the issue of hypersexuality and how we deal with it in relationships when it comes to ADHD.

What can be particularly problematic is when two sex drives aren't compatible. Granted, that's the case in any relationship, but it tends to be more of an issue in neurodivergent relationships. High sex drives can be just as awkward or cause big issues when one partner is constantly asking for hook-ups that they may not get.

In my ADHD group, Kait has been diagnosed for four years and is currently in a same-sex relationship. "Most of the time, our individual sex drives are in sync with each other, but more often than not, even when we are in the mood, we're usually way too tired to actually have sex. When our sex drives don't match, it can feel awkward and weird, but it's never something we hold against each other or resent each other for."

Ignoring the Flags

I've said elsewhere that I tend toward hyposexual rather than hypersexual. But at the beginning of a relationship, the dopamine rush we crave can mean I'm hyperfocused on being with that person. A good part of that is wanting to be intimate with them, including sex. This can also mean I've ignored the red flags in a relationship. Our brains don't want to lose that lovely hit of dopamine, so I've often thought this is why we'll come up with any excuse to ignore red flags which would have most people heading for the door.

When I've heard the death knell of a relationship in trouble, I've often simply put on my headphones and ignored it. In my relationship with S, who also has ADHD, he was the one actively avoiding sex and I was the one pretending things were fine. He was suffering with hyposexuality as a result of intense financial hardship, while pretending he was doing okay. I've often wondered if the thrill of the chase with S gave me that much needed dopamine fix, so I never grew bored of having sex with him.

I've only experienced that twice in my life, and it has always been when the other person is a bit aloof, so I feel a bit more like I have to work at their interest, which gives me that beautiful dopamine.

I spent money I didn't have on lingerie that pinched me in the wrong places, made elaborate dinners, and spent hours on date plans that never happened. In short, I tried to be the best version of my most lovable self to counteract my partner's failing interest. Now, I recognise the pattern he was exhibiting as the dialling down of hyperfocus and the start of a new panic: his money problems. He became obsessed with financial issues, and our time together was filled with conversation about the political situation and economics, but when it came to his own finances, in true ADHD male form, he hid the true extent of just how bad it was from me.

This was deep-recession Ireland. All of us were scratching and starting to become jobless during this time. S was no exception; his work went from four nights a week DJing in bars to one, if he was lucky. His side-hustle jobs melted away, taking his sanity and rent money with it.

One night, I planned the perfect meal. I went to four different shops in Limerick searching for the different courses. I spent hours preparing the food, picking my way around S's kitchen which, like all of the apartments he had ever had, was a mess. There were piles of stuff left on counters where he had been working on a thing and just left it there. A thousand tiny projects he had started but never finished in true ADHD form. The clutter drove me mad at times, but it was amusing to see that he always knew where everything was until it was time to step out of the house, and he couldn't find a

wallet or keys. I had manoeuvred my way into a
slinky black dress with a matching bra and knickers
set, complete with suspenders. What man had
ever refused suspenders? I confidently applied my
makeup, stepped into my heels, and prepared to
play the perfect host over candlelight.

It didn't work.

I ignored his sullen state and quietness over the
table, while trying to engage him in a lively dinner-
worthy chat. I worked overtime, determined that
this would fix whatever problem existed. It was
very apparent that we were in the process of falling
apart at this stage. I pushed forward with mindless
conversation I thought he might like. "I hear there's
going to be an election," I twittered then took a
sip of my wine. "Do you think we'll end up with
Fine Gael or Fianna Fáil this time?" I knew he
liked politics chat, but he was silent while pushing
vegetables around his plate. The sound of the metal
fork scraping the ceramic was the only noise he
made.

He left the table after dessert to go watch the
news in the living room. I put away plates and
cleared the table wondering why this had been left
to me. It wasn't enough that I had cooked a big
meal or sourced all the ingredients.

"Never mind that. Leave it for a bit," he
graciously called from the living room where he was
sprawled across the couch. I gave up and sat beside
him on the grey couch, draping my legs seductively
across him. I made sure he noted that I was wearing
suspenders and heels by stretching them over his
lap. There was a silence as he ignored my gesture.

After a while, he lit a cigarette for me and
another for him. The lighter made a small click as

it produced a large flame. A small gesture that defined our relationship: we were all late nights, shared cigarettes, and rounds of beer. Nothing was happening, and I was going to have to take charge. I decided now was my chance, so I took off my dress and sat there in my underwear.

He carried on watching TV.

Five minutes passed.

I waited tensely on the edge of the sofa.

He carried on watching TV.

Five more minutes passed.

I sat back beside him and draped my stocking-covered legs across his lap.

He carried on watching TV.

Another five minutes passed.

I draped my dress across myself, feeling red hot embarrassment.

He carried on watching TV.

Five more minutes.

I put my dress back on.

He carried on watching TV.

Another five minutes passed.

I gave up.

Humiliated, I went to our room and peeled off my stockings to the soundtrack of the weather report being introduced. I thought of the early days where we would have been on the sofa having sex before the film had even started, and I would have only been wearing a T-shirt and skinny jeans. Often, we would watch the film naked while smoking the same cigarette.

I now know why this happened, but at the time, I was twenty-five and unaccepting of my ADHD. I was embarrassed and ashamed that my partner didn't find me sexy. I'm also mortified that I have put others through something similar as a result of my own hyposexuality. Although S had a definite period of anxiety linked to his issues with money, he also had a fading hyperfocus as the gloss wore off our new relationship. Years later, he finally admitted to me how much financial difficulty he had been in during that time.

He had been worried about paying bills, rent, and child support. He often spoke to me about whatever was troubling him, so I never thought for one minute that he was holding back on me. He was the master at hiding his emotions or serving up small hints of financial problems deeply buried in a rant.

ADHD people can be terrible at controlling our finances. I knew S to be a very generous person; he bought shots for people on nights out and travelled out of his way to make birthday parties for people when he could barely afford the petrol. The result of those €60 rounds of Sambuca meant he was lying awake at night worrying about the rent. When you're super-focused on shit out of your control, sex isn't the first thing on your mind. And if you're not talking to your partner, then the emotional fallout is inevitable. He had stuff going on that he didn't talk about. I didn't know about that stuff, but I was feeling like crap because of his silence and distance. But then I didn't talk to him about it either. Around and around we went. Hyposexual met hypersexual, and we fizzled out.

Emotional Carnival

I experience the hyperactive unable-to-concentrate behaviour which is associated with ADHD quite often. I mean, the manic, over the top, in your face side of me that runs not walks. One side of this is my ability to channel my attention into a subject that catches my interest. I'm not about buying one red lipstick; I have to own all the possible shades of red I can find. This is one of those elements of hyperfocus.

It can be a blessing when you clean your house, or it can be a curse, like when you need to sleep after work, but there are episodes of *Bob's Burgers* you haven't watched yet. I lock onto a subject then find it impossible to break focus until one day, for no reason, I do. I have zero control over when this happens, which drives me mad.

This also happens with people.

I know that neurotypical folk also feel the love buzz in early days of relationships. It's just incredibly intense for neurodivergent folk, and we often don't know how to process what we're feeling. This lack of processing for me means I walk around and around the local estate for hours, burning off excessive manic energy while listening to music. I spend all my time texting, looking at my phone, or in-depth ranting about that thing they said that one time. It often means I text back immediately rather than playing it cool. I have, as they say, zero chill.

In fact, I can confidently say most of my family and friends know that I am always quick to come back on texts or calls. I can be relentlessly annoying and never stop. That level of intensity isn't always welcome and can be very irritating for neurotypical folk who end up asking you not to text them as much.

My friendships were like this as a child, and now I have the same thing with relationships. I can come across almost as though I'm in love without even knowing the person. The obsession (and dopamine rush) means I'll do anything to be with that person, above and beyond what I feel most neurotypical folk will do. This is why polyamory doesn't work for me—although I gave it a good go. I hyperfocus my energy into one person so there's little left for me, let alone another person.

For instance, on a whim, I once flew to New York to tell S that I loved him in person after feeling intensely that he might be my soul mate. I wasn't even deterred by the serious cost involved to do it. It just felt like a beautifully romantic gesture that would mean I'd get to experience something of life in a city that allegedly never slept.

This was my first time seeing S in two years, after the last time he left me. I had to make the right impression that would drive home that I wasn't a stressed-out student anymore but a glamorous, working person who had their life in order. I dyed my hair bright red, which was immediately ruined by a gross communal bottle of Head and Shoulders that the men kept in their bathroom. That shampoo removes colour, so by the end of the week, I was a faded flamingo rather than a bright, confident pillar box red. I was a nervous wreck. I got horrifically drunk the night before in a bid to get over my panic. "What if he doesn't turn up at the airport?" I wailed to my mother. I would have been in serious trouble, given that I was staying in his small, shared accommodation. I had no other place to go, so if he didn't arrive to collect me I'd be in trouble.

I instantly fell in love with the soul of the city because it's almost as if it's ADHD too. There's a sexy undercurrent of fun to be had, if only you could find it. It doesn't sit still for anyone and makes no apologies. Unlike London, which I can only deal with in small doses, it felt manageable and non-threatening. London carries a swagger and an edge to it that I find has me feeling nervous and alone, like anything could happen to me.

While in New York, I did some serious red-flag-ignoring as I wanted to focus on the loveliness of my reunion with this man I thought I loved. For all the long breakfasts we had gazing at each other and drinks we had where we were wrapped in our self-importance, there was a dark side. I had to ignore how, in true ADHD "doom pile" fashion, he hadn't cleaned the apartment for my arrival, to the point where I had to pick my way through a mountain of mess from the door to the bed. He often did this, where he would start one project, put it on the floor, then not finish before starting another, which also ended up on the floor. The result was complete chaos in household form.

In preparation for this reunion, I had been plucked, preened, and stripped of every last stray hair from my body before I went to meet him. He hadn't even bothered to Hoover, so the floor was covered in a gritty dirt that circled the items on the floor. "Never you mind that," said my ADHD brain cheerfully as it focused elsewhere. I noticed a condom box amongst the litter on the floor and nudged it with my foot. I could see there were two condoms in it instead of three. We hadn't had sex yet, so he hadn't used this condom with me. "Never you mind that," screamed my ADHD as the first flickers of disappointment set in.

It continued when he announced he would be going to work one night. New York is expensive, I thought to myself. He doesn't want to, but he has to. It didn't excuse the fact that I would once again be hanging around the bar while he was DJing. That can be great fun. I used to enjoy hanging around or being in the DJ booth with him while he played. I loved watching him feed off the energy of the crowd after he'd whipped them into a frenzy with a carefully chosen song. He was a master of curating the mood of a crowd, which was fascinating to watch. He would sometimes smuggle bottles of cider in his DJ bags for both of us, and we would have sneaky sips. While it was fun, it didn't excuse the fact that I was in town only for a few nights, and he hadn't bothered to book the night off. "Never you—" my ADHD started but I mentally cut it off; *Yeah, yeah, I get it.*

When it was time to leave, I stood in the departures line in JFK airport with tears streaming down my face. We held hands for as long as I could in the queue before I eventually had to leave. I came home with a case of very confusing jet lag. Hyperfocus meant I overlooked all those red flags that S kept handing me. I wonder if other ADHD folk would agree that we need to learn to acknowledge these, no matter how hard our brains try to fight them. I often say we shouldn't fight our ADHD instincts, because you can't change the way your mind is programmed. However, we need to be cautious here; some people and situations are dangerous for us. If we don't see red flags because our brain chooses not to due to its ever-present search for a dopamine hit, then shit can get real. Fast.

One of the benefits of understanding our ADHD traits better is how we can change and grow. For instance, in comparison to my situation with S, where I willingly overlooked all the negative stuff, I recently ended a relationship with someone who had started to hand me red flags. It had begun innocently enough with me thinking that their sense of humour was quite bitchy. I realised I had started to monitor my behaviour so that I wouldn't provoke them into making remarks about me, which meant I never relaxed. I was constantly on edge, ready to offer a comeback if they got too close to being offensive. Because I could never relax around them, I was exhausted every time they left my presence. Saying "sorry" over and over again became a mantra. I apologised for everything from talking to breathing near them. I needed some time alone to get my energy levels back up. It all came to a head one afternoon when I made some pasta…

I never ate or cooked in front of this person as I knew it would bring on a lot of criticism or commentary. One day, I got hungry enough that I decided to go for it and actually make some food. Nothing was good enough. They commented on everything from the pasta I selected to the water and the herbs I used. I almost didn't want the food in the end, because it had been so nerve-racking to make it while having barbs disguised as banter thrown at me. I'm very wary of anyone who uses the term banter, because it's often used when they're trying to excuse comments that are very borderline. As it was, I strongly suspect their bitching came from a place of deep insecurity instead of anything else. It was a way of coping with what life was throwing at them.

I decided then and there that whatever this thing had been, it was done for. I could never introduce

them to my friends or family for fear of that horrible
bitchy side to them. While I was physically attracted
to them, I found their personality lacking and dark.
I was finally ready to face the red flags head on
and confront them. The dopamine hit, the fear of
rejection, the hyperfocus...none of it was enough
to allow someone to treat me that way. I stopped
texting them, and they stopped texting me,
eventually fading away into the darkness where
I believe all the people I've dated go. A sort of
black hole of ex-partners where they just wander
around feeling sorry for themselves. I was so proud
of myself for recognising negativity and taking the
steps to protect myself. I would rather be single
than with someone who can't treat me properly or
makes me too nervous to make pasta. I bloody *love*
pasta.

I often find myself obsessed with someone
one month, only to never speak of them the next.
This happens with people I date too, and it can
devastate them when I break focus. That's what
happened with R. I loved her so much when we
were together, but the focus on us, our relationship,
and my first proper queer anything broke down,
and I had no idea how to fix it because I hadn't
embraced my ADHD properly. Doing that would
have meant I accepted I wasn't broken, I didn't
need fixing, and that I could take proper steps
to communicate the issues brought about by the
different aspects of my ADHD.

This hurt is usually never intentional by anyone
who is neurodiverse. It doesn't mean that one
person is the victim over the other. It simply means
that you have to find a way to co-exist and explain
this to each other. I believe R would have been

more understanding if I'd been more active in saving our relationship. Alternatively, it may just have been our time to split up. I'll never know.

In their book, *The Couple's Guide to Thriving with ADHD*, Melissa Orlov and Nancie Kohlenberger state that, "ADHD partners who have learned to live with the impact of ADHD symptoms are often oblivious to the very real emotional problems and stress their symptoms encourage in their partners. Neither partner's experience is right or wrong but it can be different."[33]

They also confirm what I often felt to be the case between me and R. "Non-ADHD partners, for example, long for attention from their ADHD partner but simultaneously fear that if they act lovingly and let up on the pressure, then their ADHD partners will revert to poor behaviours."[34] This was certainly true as R planned date nights and bath times for us, longing for that connection. I did the opposite and buried myself in work, which has long been a trigger for me based on the fear and anxiety of losing my job. Me working long hours to the point of ignoring R meant that she'd remember the long baths we took back at the start of our relationship and wonder what had happened. Truthfully, I replaced my focus on my relationship with my hyperfocus on work.

Hyperfocus is one of those things I can't explain to people who have never dealt with it. I wish I could channel it into something productive. That's where we differ with neurotypical folk who can give a normal amount of attention to something when they choose to. If I don't choose to focus on something, then nothing is going to make me do it.

Anastasia explained this to me in our Zoom call.

"ADHD people have a hard time transitioning back, whereas neurotypical people can get distracted for a period of time, but they snap back and can make their brain do stuff it doesn't want to do. That's one of the hardest things for people without ADHD to understand; it's not like that for everyone. Your brain cannot just do this."

Hyperfocus can sometimes override physical needs too. ADHD people can often forget to eat or pee because we're experiencing an intense period of concentration. When I'm falling for someone or hyperfocused on them I don't eat a lot. I like to go for long walks too where I can be alone with my thoughts. I'm a complete daydreamer who can disappear into a cloud of my own thoughts for hours while walking. I'll often come to, unsure how I ended up miles from home and what I've been doing for a few hours.

Too Loud, Too Itchy, Too Much!

Hypersensitivity affects a lot of people with ADHD. It's when things are *too much*. Noise, light, smells, touch... It's like being assaulted by the smell of cinnamon, and the scratch of a clothing label, and the drip of a faucet, all at the same time. But much, much worse. It comes in many forms, and like all aspects of ADHD/neurodiversity, some people experience these differently than others.

With regard to sex, I've heard of hypersensitivity that makes genital stimulation uncomfortable or even painful. It's when I do a bit of reading that I see something of myself in it. The website Medical News Today has this snippet: "This sensitivity may also extend to other senses as well. Smells or tastes associated with sex may reduce arousal or make it difficult for a person to focus on the act itself, which may lead to difficulties in staying aroused."[35]

This has happened to me before, where a smell or a sound has been overwhelming. I'm currently living in a terraced house jammed between two others. In the left house are an elderly couple who are practically silent. I occasionally hear them praying and chanting, but that's about it. The right house has small children that are the absolute antichrist. I am consistently bombarded with banging, clashing, and screaming. I'm not one to insult a small child, but there are occasions where only a swear word will do.

I have on occasion blasted Slayer to drown out the sounds of their five-year-old screaming, "1...2...3...4... HIDE AND SEEK." Lockdown made me do things I'm not proud of, like getting into noise battles with five-year-olds and buying tie-dye boiler suits I will *never* wear.

While I'm not the only one in a city who suffers from noisy neighbours, noise does affect me and can overwhelm me completely on occasion. Smells can do that too, where I become obsessed with the smell in the room. When I'm tired, this is even worse, and I lose any ability to filter out these things. It becomes the only thing I can focus on, even if there's nothing I can do about it.

Does this mean I can only have sex in a room where all the smells and sounds are eliminated? Therefore ruling out my own noisy home? Well, yes, it might do.

I'm not saying that every sexual encounter is going to need specialist lighting or a scented candle...but whatever it takes. Sometimes, at the start of a relationship when things are really fresh, and we have that throw-down energy with our chosen person, then it's easier to ignore these things. I find I'm more focused on seeking intimacy with a person at that stage than I am worried about my own pleasure. Maybe that's actually quite depressing when you think about it. I've become accustomed to giving in to my ADHD and ignoring my own pleasure. This is usually the moment where a "helpful" neurotypical will suggest getting a daily planner or making a time schedule. I refuse to believe that we need to plan out our decision to have sex.

I know when I planned to have sex with R, something else would happen. My mind would switch off, and the excuses would start to roll in. I would mentally set time aside to have sex. "Tonight is the night. I'll do it after work," I'd tell myself as if I was gearing up to do a tax return or a smear test. Then, as the night went on, nothing would happen. So setting time aside doesn't work for me.

Hyperarousal is another thing that comes close to explaining the rush of emotions that ADHD people feel. Psychiatrist William Dodson defines hyperarousal in *ADDitude* this way: "People with ADHD have passionate thoughts and emotions that are more intense than those of the average person. Their highs are higher, and their lows are lower. This means you may experience both happiness and criticism more powerfully than your peers and loved ones do."[36] Note that although the word arousal is being used, it's not just about sex; it's about all the emotions surrounding romance in general.

I believe that hyperarousal is another reason why we intensely feel romantic emotions more than neurotypical folk do. This is why my relationships with other ADHD individuals are far more intense. My greatest example of this is what I felt for S. The connection and rush we felt for each other was heightened, and the level of intensity I normally have in relationships was reciprocated. We never spoke about ADHD, but it was a big part of the electric connection between us. Was it real or the dopamine? I have no idea, but I was having too much fun to find out. I physically craved the excitement of the situations we would find ourselves in.

What goes up must of course come down. When we're done with something, we're done. This is why I have a graveyard of hobbies in my parents' house, where lies the remains of my singing trophies, books on fashion design, or my various painting supplies. I feel like we can do this with people too. When the shine is gone, it's gone. It can often feel like this is it, we've found the one, because of the confusing rush of emotions.

Almost overnight, the hyperfocus was broken between me and S. Sadly, understanding why someone does it doesn't make it any easier when it happens to you. It's still incredibly hurtful to experience someone going from zero to sixty and back to zero in terms of their feelings for you.

S was hyperfocused on me until one day, he just wasn't. We had been obsessed with each other for months on end. We were practically living with each other and went everywhere as a pair. If you wanted one of us, you got the other too in an intense package deal that sometimes our friends didn't ask for.

We get a dopamine hit from being around

people we like, which makes us feel blissfully happy. Imagine the dopamine hit you get from ADHD hyperarousal. I would love to see some studies on this that included actual women, non-binary, transgender, and queer people rather than just the usual ADHD men. The closest I can describe this feeling to neurotypical folk is that it feels a lot like the nervous energy that comes with chronic anxiety.

Imagine that nervous, sick, tense, twitchy feeling that you get with internalised anxiety, but it's about the person you love. And you hyperfocus on it, so that it's all you think about and feel.

You're welcome.

Some researchers believe that unmedicated ADHD adults have lower concentrates of proteins in the brain called dopamine transporters (referred to as dopamine transporter density). Dopamine is a neurotransmitter that allows us to regulate our emotional responses to things, giving us feelings of pleasure and happiness as a reward.[37] There are also some links to serotonin which is responsible for happiness, suggesting we may also have lower amounts of this mood-stabilising chemical produced in the brain. Yet another reason for seeking out happiness boosts where we can. Both serotonin and dopamine play roles in keeping us calm, focused, and chill. Although when they are disrupted, our anxiety and trouble concentrating increases along with unhappiness.

We tend to have lower levels of dopamine in our brains, which means we often seek out things which can give us a quick hit to keep us topped up. This can include risky behaviours such as sex, drug-taking, or bar-hopping, but there are plenty of others too.

Anastasia, an ADHD life coach, explains why this is particularly dangerous for adults who have just been diagnosed. "The older ADHD people get, the more certain behaviours can become destructive. The interesting thing is those certain behaviours can also be your superpower. There are statistics on ADHD and self-medicating behaviours or self-stimulating behaviours such as unsafe sex, drugs, or alcohol to gambling. If those things don't end, then as soon as you become an adult, they could get worse."

A very early study that examined dopamine transporter density in humans revealed a 70% increase in six of the adults with ADHD. This was in comparison to the ones who didn't have ADHD.[38]

The higher concentration of dopamine transporters removes dopamine from brain cells. The more of them there are, then the quicker they remove the dopamine, meaning it has less time to do anything positive. These low levels of dopamine are the reason why stimulants are prescribed to some adults. They increase dopamine levels and bring us up to the same level that neurotypical people are at.[39]

I was on stimulant medications as a child. I remember next to nothing of the experience. I was told however that Ritalin had little effect on me. I've not been put on medication in the UK—yet. I have asked but so far, nothing has happened. The broken system means that as I type, there is a two-year wait for ADHD and autism diagnoses in Nottingham. All diagnoses need to be made by a psychologist rather than your local GP. The huge increase in ADHD interest through awareness, visibility, TikTok, and more has created a surge that the services, post-COVID, can't deal with. Many of us are left in the system waiting on medication or diagnosis.

Risky Business

I had felt confident that I would be fine when it came to the issue of risk-taking. After all, I have a certain level of "Cop on," as we say in Ireland, which means I'm careful, right? RIGHT?

I now live as a non-binary, queer person, which means I have a certain level of risk where my very visibly queer appearance is too extreme for some, so I have to be careful where I go or who I kiss in public. But surely, as I date non-binary people and women, I should be safer than I would be dating men, right? I would do well to remember that even our community has predators, abusers, and scary people in it. The risk might look different, but it's still there regardless of how many rainbow flags we slap on it.

The more I researched into risky behaviours for ADHD, the more I felt deeply uncomfortable. I spotted some of them popping up in my own life story, and the reason I am safer now is down to experience.

I'm lucky that I've never had an STD, but I have had an abortion that came from taking risks with men in a country that had no safety net. Until I was in my early thirties and had figured my sexuality out, I dated men and women, so I used condoms where I needed to. The pregnancy happened as a result of failed contraceptives rather than no contraceptives, but there was a risk calculation there. I did this knowing that I was living in a country that wouldn't provide any help or support for me if I did get pregnant.

The red flags that I discussed earlier are one way in which our dopamine-seeking behaviours can bulldoze over fact. Another way it does this is to affect how we calculate risky sexual behaviour, meaning that we might acknowledge them briefly but plough straight through to get to the other side. We also simply can't fully assess what the other side is going to look like, so we don't see the future properly.

A study in the *Frontiers in Psychology* in 2019 talks about this risk behaviour: "People with ADHD tend to engage in risk-taking behaviours, defined as behaviours associated with a higher probability of undesirable outcomes, such as significant physical injuries or financial loss. These risk-taking behaviours include, among others, substance use, smoking, reckless driving, and sexual risk-taking behaviour (SRTB). Sexual risk-taking behaviour may result in a variety of undesirable outcomes, including family conflicts, financial loss, and damaged reputation, but the two most commonly addressed concerns are unintended pregnancies and sexually transmitted diseases, such as HIV/ AIDS (Turchik and Garske, 2009). SRTB involves having sex at an early age, having unprotected sex, and having multiple sexual partners (Martinez et al., 2011). These health-threatening behaviours have been linked to drug and alcohol abuse, psychopathology, early parenthood, educational problems, and convictions."[40]

It continues: "A recent study examined whether the link between ADHD symptoms and the overall level of risk-taking behaviour is explained by differences in benefit and risk perceptions and attitudes. The study found a positive correlation between ADHD symptoms and the level of benefit perception. Furthermore, a mediation analysis revealed an indirect pathway between ADHD and risk-taking behaviour through increased benefit perception, suggesting that people with ADHD engage in risk-taking behaviour more often than controls, since they view the benefits of engaging in these risky behaviours as greater."

Melissa Orlov and Nancie Kohlenberger in *The Couple's Guide to Thriving With ADHD*, also confirm that ADHD people tend to process things differently to those without. "People with ADHD tend to live in the moment. They tend to go with the flow and react to their environment. Those without ADHD spent a good deal of time anticipating what will happen next."[41]

I asked around the group of ADHD people I interviewed about how they perceived their risk-taking behaviours and if they took what they thought were high risks.

Kelsey, a twenty-seven-year-old person told me, "I did in my early twenties as I was compulsive and didn't commonly use protection. My sex drive is equal parts high and low, depending on how I am feeling that day or how my mind is focusing that day. I also suffer from post-traumatic stress disorder (PTSD) which includes sexual trauma. I feel both the ADHD and PTSD play a part in my sex drive."

I'm aware that my asking people about this can have a dark side and can trigger bad memories for people. It could make people think about times that consent may not have been given. Impulsive behaviours can lead to other situations that are less than ideal. I claim to not see red flags in relationships, but I often don't see them in situations either. While unwanted pregnancies and STDs are a consequence of taking a risk with a person, there are also ways in which taking a risk with a situation can lead to things like assault or rape.

My decisions that can be described as risky often involved alcohol. I am a lover of the good times, and my hyperactivity means I love being out of the house. I am often, even now, out several times a week, having pints or meals with friends, or going to cinema or burlesque evenings on a school night. I am the worst for getting one for the road before I head home. While that sometimes means I'll just have to deal with a hangover the next morning, other decisions I've made horrify me to this day.

G was an Italian friend I'd met in my early days of moving to Dublin. Tall, loud, and opinionated, he had originally driven me insane when I first met him. My original assessment of him was that he was awful. "I don't want him anywhere near me," I told my partner. He was pushy and obnoxious but barged into my life regardless. He set off several red flags when we hung out, causing me to cringe internally at how people must see him and, by extension, me. He treated shop assistants like they were beneath him by shouting abuse and being rude. I did my usual trick of ignoring entitled behaviour like this and carried on hanging out with him to avoid being impolite.

I was new to the city, so I didn't know anyone. While my partner was at work, I was left bored and alone at home. I hung out with anyone who would give me the time of day.

Over the years, living in Nottingham mellowed G as he got used to being in a relaxed city full of diversity. His town in Italy was tiny with very few gay people, so he could be homophobic at times. His sense of entitlement and loudness quietened to a point where I felt he was almost a different person. We went drinking together occasionally over the years, and he brought me home numerous times in bad states. He would put me to bed, bring me water, and make sure I took sips before he left so I wouldn't die a small death in the morning. I became part of a friend group with him; I knew his girlfriend and he knew my partner. This somehow made me trust him even more, because he respected "bro-code" and would never violate my trust or my partner's.

So when another random week night turned into drinks, I didn't even think about my full shift at the magazine I had just started working at the next day. I found myself drinking with him and thinking nothing of it. Pints turned into strong weed with two other men I had never met before. It didn't matter to me that I was due in the newsroom in the early hours; I'd done this countless times while inhaling Haribo sweets to keep myself on the high that early starts demanded of me. I had tomorrow to deal with that. While we rolled joints and listened to loud music, the room started to spin violently as the weed and pints mixed in my system. I was an experienced drinker, so I had a high tolerance, but this time, I wasn't going to make it. I spent some time on the floor in his bathroom, vomiting cider into the bowl while acknowledging I couldn't move.

The men left, and G knelt beside me on the tile floor. "Oh my god, you are so drunk." He laughed while stroking my hair back. "You can stay here if you want, save getting a taxi in case you're sick again."

I failed to consider the consequences of what could happen if I stayed. I trusted my friend, which isn't my fault. Victims of sexual assault are not to be blamed for the actions of their attacker. I do believe that my ADHD combined with the drink made the risk less apparent to me though. I didn't see that I was sharing a bed with a man whose behaviour could sometimes be problematic.

I climbed into his double bed, because there was nowhere else to stay in his tiny city centre accommodation. I kept my clothes on and happily passed out almost immediately, feeling relieved I was safe. When I woke up, I knew instantly something wasn't right. A hand was under my top, touching my breasts over my bra. I froze in shock. I have no sense as to how long I stayed like that, willing him to stop. My mind started to scream about what could happen if this continued. Would he rape me? I had no way of knowing, and no one knew where I was. I faked waking up and felt relief as his hand rapidly withdrew from my clothes.

The next morning, I was confused, hungover, and in the horrors about what happened. I started to doubt myself as my mind pushed the memory of his hands away. I ignored the assault frighteningly easily. I excused myself to leave, and he begged to come with me. I was too polite or too frightened to say no, so less than twenty-four hours after he'd attacked me, I took him to work with me. Clutching a coffee, I nearly fainted when my editor introduced himself to G and struck up a conversation with him.

"This man has assaulted me," I pictured myself screaming in an alternate universe. But I stood there watching him poke around my desk. It was two years before I mentioned this to anyone and five years before I used the word assault. I never spoke to him about it, and it was five years before I cut him out of my life completely. I watch him meet my parents on the street in Nottingham when we're out shopping and meet him by accident. My soul leaves my body as he shakes my father's hand.

I'm not saying that sexual assault happens to only ADHD people, obviously, but we need to be aware that our risk-taking behaviours can make it more of a possibility. I took a risk staying with someone I trusted, and I didn't think this could happen to someone like me, by someone like him, in a place like that. I paid dearly for that. For years I convinced myself that it hadn't actually happened, and the weed and drink combined to make me hallucinate.

It's easy to blame yourself for situations like this. To think about that split-second decision you made, and then society tells victims of sexual assault or rape that they were the ones in the wrong. No one should ever feel shame or be silenced for this. Those who commit these crimes know how to spot opportunity or vulnerability and exploit it. I stand on the side of the victim, unquestioningly and always believing. Risk-taking behaviours don't make it your *fault*. Never think that.

A scary thought occurred to me that drinking, sex with the wrong person, and the potential of STDs aren't the only place where I've taken risks. I've also taken part in kink, fetishism, and BDSM over the years. Those activities in themselves aren't risky, clearly; it's a subculture steeped in rules and social parameters. But how and with whom…that's where it can get shady.

Over the years, I've learned how to be cautious

even if I can't calculate risk properly. The lessons I've learned from taking risks without fear have left me with very real scars that, even as an adult, I can't get rid of. Mindfulness is a blessing, but it's really hard to do with ADHD when your dopamine-seeking brain is loudly telling you to JUST DO IT.

The only thing that has worked for me has been a combination of bad experiences, lessons learned, and slowing down to think. It can feel almost painful when I have to force my brain to stop and slow down for a hot minute. I have to force my brain to think things through, which I've also, embarrassingly, translated into list-making. It doesn't work all the time, but when it has, I'm grateful, because we also have to accept that we make mistakes and sometimes, it's not *just* the fault of ADHD. But thankfully, taking that extra time has saved me a bit of pain, as well as a few dodgy tattoos, over the years.

Chapter Six
Chain Reaction: How Kinky Sex Can Help Us

I was a shop worker/makeup artist/counter girl/ trainee journalist for a brief period of my life. To anyone who has worked in retail while trying to carve out a career for yourself, then that slash is the most important thing you own, and you wear it with pride. You cling to it in the hopes that someday you won't have to use it again.

I'd turned myself into a punk parody during this time, with wild hair that stood up in multi-coloured spikes, elaborate makeup in bold tones that framed my eyes or overwhelmed my cheekbones, and I wore all black everything. I was desperately unhappy as I imagined I'd never be the full-time journalist I wanted to be.

If I'm setting the scene, then my job isn't the only thing that you should know about me at this point. I was post-breakup with a person I'd been forcing a happy household with, despite their problematic on/off drinking and subsequent relapse into alcoholism. As a response, I'd taken up dating someone who was emotionally unavailable, which was fine as I wasn't ready to be in a proper relationship with anyone. I was trapped in my life but mostly, I felt like I was failing at being an adult and had become an embarrassment to my family. I had imagined that I would be wildly successful or married or both. This wasn't what my life was supposed to look like. Instead of domestic bliss, in under a month, I'd moved back into a house share to live with three strangers, single-parenting a small, very ill cat, and I was on my own again.

Same old, same old.

It was another Saturday at the makeup store with my brush belt strapped around my waist, and I watched the customers mingle around the lipstick counters in the centre of the store. I was having a conversation with a colleague when I casually reached up and rested my arms on the ceiling. I'm quite tall, so this wasn't a drastic stretch but a pleasant one that helped me to take the weight off my feet a bit. There was an audible gasp from the other artist as my sleeve rolled back a bit.

"What happened to your arm?" she asked curiously.

She stared at the underside of my left arm, which was now exposed as my shirt had rolled back when I moved. I hadn't realised that the underside of my arm was covered in violent-looking bite marks. There were deepish red wounds in a row against the pale white skin of my arm, and they were set off by the spread of blueish bruising. I thought about blaming the cat but realised that there was no way they were small enough to belong to a kitten.

"It's nothing bad," I said, forcing a fake laugh. "I was completely into it." I prayed she wouldn't repeat it to anyone, let alone HR. I realised slowly that she hadn't jumped to the correct conclusion that I had just had a night of rough sex; she thought I had been attacked.

Now here is the truth:

I like kink.

I like to be bitten.

I like slaps.

I never, until researching this, realised that I use this type of sex occasionally to help with my ADHD. In fact, if no one minds too much (and really, even if they do), I'm going to controversially argue that I believe this type of sex has helped me in lots of ways. I need to state up front that I don't consider being kinky, into fetish, or BDSM anything to be ashamed of. I've done far worse in life than sniff poppers or pee on people, but this is hardly the time or place to list the more outrageous things I took part in when at art college. There's no better place to experiment than that.

Once upon a time, I dated men. As time passed, I felt that this no longer was something I wanted in life and which, possibly, hadn't ever been the right thing for me. I have loved some wonderful men but ultimately, my heart isn't in it. One thing I will say is that my general experience has been with men when it comes to these sexual experiences. While queer folk also engage in these practises, I haven't yet. I don't have an excuse or reason for this. This is one area in which it is what it is. So the below is specific to my experiences with men. Maybe one day I'll get to write another book about kink and queerness.

It's worth noting that along with the mention of men, this chapter is going to talk about consent and what some may consider rough sex. But everything I've done has been with loving, experienced, and wonderful partners I have very much consented to.

While researching risky ADHD behaviour, my mind went to dark places concerning consent. I wondered if I could ever truly consent to riskier acts with a partner if I don't fully process risks like others. I pondered this for weeks, feeling scared and wondering where my line was. I realised ultimately that what mattered here was practising consent (always) but also mindful sex.

The risk I'm referring to concerns the issue that strangers or partners may not stop when you drop the safe word, or that you sign up for things you may not feel comfortable with. While I agree that getting out of your comfort zone sexually is a good thing on a Friday night every now and again, it's a conversation first arrangement.

I've had one partner who fully understood how to nurture a connection through BDSM and practise it safely. They introduced me to things I had never experienced before but took the time to explain how they worked and what we were doing, and we had a better time as a result.

In fact, in a dodgy hotel in Manchester, we had a laugh as they fitted my body with tight purple ropes that bit into my skin. They showed me how to build up to steady spanking and how to tie the most beautiful knots. We communicated first, during and after, about how it felt so the risk was massively diminished. If I said our agreed safe word, they would stop immediately.

But what happens if the risk is part of the kink or the person is a stranger to you?

BDSM, kink, or fetish isn't wrong nor are they dirty or weird. I refuse to apologise for ropes, feel guilty for gimp masks, or bad for using ball gags. Life is too short not to sexually try everything on the menu at least once…or more if you like it.

I believe sex like this with strangers, or new partners, or where a risk is involved means we need to practice mindful sex. This expression came to me when I found an article on *ADDitude* magazine about speaking to your ADHD teenager about sex. While I'm not about to speak to any teenagers about sex, it gave me the words to describe having a good, honest, frank conversation with yourself. "Smart sex education for teens with ADHD should focus, first and foremost, on mindfulness. This doesn't mean your child must meditate before kissing his boyfriend for the first time! Rather, it means that before engaging in any sexual activity, your teen should ask himself: 'Is this what I want to be doing? Am I making this decision for me, or because some outside force is influencing me? Will I look back on this positively five years from now?'"[42]

I believe that ADHD people need to take time to consider what is being asked of us. We need to ask if we are okay with it and if it's actually something we want. The right person will understand, and the right situation will mean that you will feel comfortable or relaxed. Anyone who pressures you into doing anything sexual you don't want to do can get in the bin.

Kink can have positive effects for ADHD people. I am conscious that kink, fetish, and the wonderful world of whips can have a bad name, so I want to highlight that there are schools of thought that are pro-pain, pro-Dom, and pro-queer experiences of BDSM for those of us who are a little bit different.

After all, life is short...buy the harness.

Besides the potential for a good time, there are lots of benefits to having this sort of sex or relationship with a person.

I find that it can help me stay grounded in my body when my mind starts to wander. My mind wandering during sex can bring a certain level of embarrassment. I feel a shame internally that yet again I've been mentally begging my partner to finish quickly as I'm bored or because I can't focus on my lovely, wonderful partner because I'm not present. This means I struggle to orgasm when I'm with someone. I don't think I had appreciated how strange this might be to neurotypical women who can also struggle with orgasm but still experience it. If you, as an ADHD person, don't want to focus, then nothing will make you, and this is true even when it comes to sex. There are ADHD people who don't struggle with orgasms, but I do wonder if there's a higher percentage of sex without orgasms compared to our neurotypical friends.

When it comes to BDSM and grounding our tired ADHD brains, I asked my group of ADHD people. Kari, a pansexual thirty-four-year-old woman summed it up perfectly. "Some light choking, spanking, and heavy physical touch helps snap me back to reality, so I can focus more on what's happening in the moment. Slow, easy vanilla-type stuff lets my mind wander, so sometimes a sudden shock to my physical body can help bring me back and make it more enjoyable. Sometimes playing as a submissive to get ordered around [helps too], more so because I don't know what to do with myself."

I spoke to Morgan, a twenty-year-old lesbian who was diagnosed at seven years old. "Another thing that helps my ADHD and keeps me focused on what's going on during sex is restraints. I think having the feeling of the restraints constantly on me helps me stay focused, because it's also like a reminder."

I have found that there is little understanding of the loathing and shame that this lack of concentration makes us feel, even subconsciously. In the past, I have allowed myself to have sex where I am there in body but not in mind. I made noises, gasped, groaned, and ran my nails down backs knowing that, when asked, I would have to lie and say I came. I have turned to drink in the past to dull the noise, lights, and distractions of literally everything around me, so I feel more capable of staying in the moment.

It's that staying in the moment that kink can help us with, especially in moments of exhaustion or being overwhelmed. I can feel physically exhausted by the overwhelming stimulation of being ADHD. I can get so tired from all of the noise, lights, and life ganging up on me and overwhelming my senses. The closest thing that I have read that describes this overwhelming sensation comes from a book on autism which has nothing to do with sex. I strongly believe autism is closely related to ADHD in so many ways. We have a lot of shared traits, which means in researching this book, I've come across autism writing that I relate to. Sadly, there is a lot less out there about ADHD in comparison. Some of these shared traits can be executive functioning difficulties, repetitive behaviours, difficulties tolerating uncertainty, or experiencing sensory difficulties.

In her book, *Odd Girl Out: An Autistic Woman in a Neurotypical World*, Laura James writes about her later in life autism diagnosis. While she isn't talking about ADHD here, I feel myself in this piece.

"I'm exhausted when I arrive back to King's Cross. I begin to feel a tell-tale prickliness inside. It begins in my chest and radiates through my arms. My senses are heightened. The sound of a man coughing is rebounding in my head. The scrape of suitcase wheels on the shiny station floor. The station announcements. The lights are too bright, the sounds too loud. The smell of fast food is cloying. I feel like I can't escape."[43]

These feelings are part of why I love BDSM. I often find relief in handing the sometimes physical, sometimes emotional reins over to someone I trust. Rather than focusing on an unpleasant sound or crack in the ceiling, my brain rushes to the feeling of someone biting me or slapping me. I'm back in the room as if I had never left. It's also delightful not to have to think as I'm told what to do.

KNEEL.

SIT.

BEG.

PLEAD.

TOUCH.

Outside the kink scenes, my mind will wander, and that isn't anyone's fault. It's not my lack of interest in the person sexually nor is it their fault for not stimulating me enough. I can't stop it or change it. In the past, neurotypical folk have said, "Why not just concentrate on staying focused and in the moment?" *No* is the long and short answer for that. I feel my lack of concentration is why I have had very few orgasms with other people in my life and why my relationships have broken down. But, by all means, tell me again how I can just force myself to be *less* ADHD. When someone offers me the chance to sit back, relax, and let them make the decisions, I jump at it. The control experienced as an ADHD submissive isn't just the thrill of *being* controlled, it's also the absolute relief in being allowed to switch off even just for a few minutes. Let someone else worry about what I experience for a while.

I note that I have this type of sex more commonly after a meaningful relationship breakup. My brain will not be at its finest hour, so I seek out someone with whom I can have a mini relationship-rebound situation, where I know that this person and I won't be long term. I do practise parts of BDSM with my long-term partners but while my brain recovers, I'll need a little bit more than I normally do to help bring my head into the game.

I also wonder, subconsciously, if some of this is me punishing myself through pain for the failure of yet another relationship. But that's another book, or at the very least, some expensive therapy.

So why didn't I introduce this with my failing relationships if it's truly something that I can lose myself in? The honest truth is that I don't have an answer to that, and sometimes it came down to sheer laziness and tiredness. It can take a lot of energy to get a harness properly set up, let me tell you. I also think there's a lot to be said for not recognising that this was helping me, because I didn't understand properly what it was doing for me. When I was away from the moment, I would think about it as just a bit of fun rather than something that really helped me to stay connected to a partner.

When I came across the ADHD and BDSM writing of blogger Joy Asitflies, I got goosebumps because I felt seen. Prior to this, I'd wondered if maybe it was just me reading too much into my desire for kinky sex or needing to somehow justify it. Joy wrote the post *How BDSM helps me to manage my ADHD* on the sex blog, *Chronic Sex*.

Joy wrote, "As someone with a diagnosis of ADHD, there are lots of things about BDSM which give me a rest from my super-busy brain. My favourite is the effect that a really heavy impact scene will have on my thought processes: the feeling of calm and focus as I wait for a paddle to land beats anything I've managed to attain in years of committed meditation practice."[44]

This is exactly my previous point about how ADHD folk can mesh with kinkier sex. I like to hand over control to more dominant people who can recognise when I need a reminder to focus.

I feel a relief that comes with acceptance that I'm not over thinking it, or that I'm some form of part-time pervert. In an article about BDSM and mental health for *Refinery 29*, Yasmin Lajoie interviewed women about their experience combining kink with their mental health. "Eevi* is a twenty-four-year-old woman who talks enthusiastically and expressively about BDSM, despite describing herself as a newbie. 'I've always been a high energy, nervous person. I got into a lot of trouble at school for not being able to focus, for lashing out. I had anger management issues and was diagnosed with ADHD,' she tells me. 'As a teenager, I spiralled. I developed anorexia. Looking back, I think it was a way for me to reclaim control. BDSM is a way for me to reclaim that control in a healthier way. It allows me the possibility of healing from bad experiences, including the rape I endured when I was eighteen. I've known I was sexually submissive from a young age, but after I was raped, it took on a deeper meaning.'"[45]

When it comes to reading about ADHD and sex, self-help books are no help at all. And this is one of the ways in which I feel current ADHD study has let us down. My argument will always be for ADHD women, transgender, and non-binary people to be more vocal, louder, and to demand spaces be made for neurodiverse folk. Although I fully acknowledge that being vocal is exhausting. We need more blog posts, essays, books, and sites about ADHD for adults who want to know how the condition affects their daily lives, especially when it comes to things like sex or relationships. I'm tired of ADHD books being written by people who do not have ADHD. More than that, I'm tired of ADHD books being written by the type of person who appears to have never had a dirty, sweaty, stinky fuck in their lives.

That said, there are things to be learned by them. In reading these books, I realised I didn't see my own self reflected there. I didn't see a mention of one bite mark or boobs. It encouraged me to write, because I knew other ADHD people who were queer, sexual, and kinky humans. Where were all of us in these books? The research that's there is valid, but so much of it is focused on relationships, sensual touching, and heterosexual sex. There is no mention of whips and chains, no inclusion of piss play, and as far as I know, there is nothing out there including strap-ons.

Melissa Orlov and Nancie Kohlenberger explain my lack of attention perfectly in *Couples Guide to Thriving with ADHD*, but this book, good as it is, sadly backs my point about the lack of kink, has no mention of homosexuality, or pages dedicated to connecting with your partner. Sex is just one small chapter shoved to the back of the book: "Just because the person wants to pay attention to something doesn't mean that he or she will be able to do so at that moment."[46]

Don't I know it.

Strategies for concentration are mentioned in a lot of ADHD self-help books. Strategies and checklists for organisation feel like a neurotypical person telling an ADHD person to "just get a planner" when we fail to be organised as a result of our ADHD. It's frustrating and unhelpful. They're also not sexy when it comes time to have sex, nor is their suggestion to take medication before you plan to have sex. Urgh.

I'm not sure I agree that scheduling sexy time around my medication is the way to go but then again, I'm a leftie vegetarian who pops CBD instead of pain medication. I already mentioned the suggestion about running a 10k race together to "bond with my partner." I think I'll take the medication, thanks.

This is where a lack of clear, fun, and chatty research causes a problem. I don't want a self-help book telling me (in a binary sexuality and gender sense) how to cope with my ADHD by stroking my partner sensually. I want a book written by another ADHD person that asks, "Are you struggling to come? Because I am and it sucks." I think that a lot of books on this subject assume that us neurodivergent folk aren't interested in sex, or it's simply too embarrassing a subject for these writers to discuss. We don't get what we don't ask for.

Not to mention, a lot of the research out there is gatekeeper-y when it comes to language. I got so tired of shifting through heavy texts about the psychological effects of ADHD by professionals. I desperately wanted a funny, easy to read book that I could pick up and put down when I felt like it. I'm really fortunate to have a post-graduate education. Although I didn't finish my PhD, I got used to reading academic language and studies, yet I find it tedious. If you've had a long day with kids and responsibilities then the last thing you want is to research your own medical condition and be confronted by tons of long words. It forces people online where they're faced with potentially misleading, false news about ADHD.

In saying that, ADHD and sex-positive blogging has given me the insight I crave into my condition. I didn't hear myself or other neurodivergent represented until I went off the beaten track and dived into the world of anonymous sex blogging.

When Self-help Books Aren't Helping

There's a disconnect between the American-style self-help books being published and the sex-positive women and queer people I see online through blogs and forums. The research is focused on heterosexuality and sex with the lights off. This is because print dominates, as does a degree in psychology or psychiatry, so these are the default voices we're hearing in the mainstream while others with voices like ours go unnoticed and unheard. Even worse than that, in 2023 we are hearing very anti-ADHD voices amplified in the media, and they're casting doubt on our condition, our lives, and our diagnosis. By all means, be sceptical of the NHS waiting times because they are awful, but leave those of us trying to live our lives out of it.

This has a knock-on effect for those of us who are lying there in the wet patch thinking, "Oh god, is it me?" It's damaging because we simply can't access help or information that looks and feels real. It took me until I was thirty-one before I asked if my ADHD could be the reason I have issues with sex and orgasm. It was another four years until I realised it could be the reason why I have relationship issues too. And I was thirty-five before I realised that BDSM helps me to stay grounded in my body, in the room, and focused.

I'm not alone in wanting to see myself represented in ADHD published work. I want to see queer representation, non-binary, transgender, and female identities shown, but there are also other issues of minority representation too. The tide is turning though.

The Norwegian artist Nora Nord has an entire project dedicated to photographing queer ADHD people, a sea of faces who are many different skin tones and abilities or sizes. Nora was motivated by her own experiences as a queer ADHD woman to start photographing people who were typically not included in mainstream photography. Her work features portraits of people staring confidently at the camera in various poses surrounded by messy homes or partners.

She told *ID* magazine in an interview: "There's a lot of misinformation about the condition and there's just so much that's left out. Even a lot of books written about ADHD are by people who don't have ADHD, or they're just geared towards cis men."[47]

I reached out to Nora as I was curious about this gorgeous series of photos. I wanted to know what she wanted people to take away from the series. "I hope more people can see themselves and it can help in any stage of ADHD," she says. "I started making this project because I wanted to see more stories about ADHD represented, and to create something that people around me with ADHD could relate with. I hope, above all, that people who see this work can recognise themselves and that it can help them too. I hope they can learn useful habits and tools to help deal with the less great parts of ADHD, so they can use their creative beautiful minds to do the amazing things they are capable of."

Nora is in the process of starting a podcast dedicated to ADHD education. She believes that diversity is essential if more people are going to seek a diagnosis. "There are so many reasons why expanding representation is crucial in ADHD representation. I think the core reason is that it means more people will recognise their own ADHD and seek support or help. When I was diagnosed, I didn't find any representation and had to work hard to recognise how it affected me. Since sharing the portrait series about queer and trans people with ADHD, I've had several people reach out to me via Instagram to say that the photos helped them to realise they had ADHD."

She added: "Representation is also another way to reduce stigma and get people talking. Visibility helps those who suffer in silence and wonder why their circular brains don't work as well in the square productivity society as those around them. We need an intersectional approach that takes into account all perspectives, because ADHD looks different in everyone."

I absolutely agree with this. If you don't see yourself in things, it can prevent people from going for help. Books that don't discuss real, dirty, filthy sex for people with ADHD are only addressing part of the problem. In fact, there's an assumption across the board that talking about sex and disabilities needs to have a *careful now* approach. The absolute nerve to assume that disabled folk don't enjoy BDSM or kinkier behaviours.

I originally met with Jennie Williams from the charity, Enhance the UK to discuss sex toys for that part of the book. Enhance the UK is a user-led charity that aims to change the way people view disability. They have recently set up Love Lounge, a section where people can go to discuss sex in all its glory.

Over Zoom, Jennie told me that they work with occupational therapists (OT) and are actively working to talk about things like BDSM or bondage kits. "This is why we love our resident OT, because she will reference this bit of bondage kit, which is brilliant for people who have spasms, as it can be used as a springboard. We've recently created some resources about bondage and how you can use that or adapt it in everyday sex. There are some people who want that lovely tenderness but sometimes... you know, everyone is different."

A quick look on Love Lounge tells me that they're not afraid to discuss complex subjects. Some of the Q&A topics online are *How to have sex when you have a stoma* or *Lesbian sex and cerebral palsy*, which are incredible. It's taken a while for conversations like this to be open, loud, and proud but I'm pleased to see they're happening.

Now, let's get these same conversations going for neurodivergent people.

Learning the Ropes...and Whips...and Chains

I was sixteen when I first practised a bit of BDSM,
albeit accidentally. My parents had agreed to
drive me to the city so I could spend some time
celebrating my results from the junior certificate.
The junior cert is a bit of a practice run for the
leaving certificate which you take at the end of your
schooling to get into college in Ireland. It would
have been 2001, so I'm almost afraid to think what
I was wearing as that era wasn't kind to us when
it came to clothing. I do remember fashioning a
necklace out of a pink chain that I had lying around.
It was tightly wound around my neck with a long
piece that ran down my chest—not unusual for me
as I was starting to experiment with drag looks at
school discos. I would go to our local under-age
disco with my face painted blue for no reason. The
local bullies weren't really sure what was happening
or how to bully accordingly, so I was mostly left
alone.

I loved being out in the city. I can't remember a
thing about where I went or what I did that night.
I would imagine not a lot as I didn't have ID or a
ticket to an event. I also didn't drink either, so god
knows what I was up to. One thing I do remember is
my partner's decision to use my necklace as a lead
and collar by pulling on it repeatedly to drag me
around. It was a thrillingly strange sight to see two
teenagers walking around Cork City at night with
one of them on a lead. Later, as an adult, I bought a
proper lead and collar to experiment with.

I feel like my position in the queer community as
a queer, non-gender conforming person has meant
that I've been exposed to the kink community

sooner than my hetero counterparts may have. Queer theory, and indeed queer BDSM theory, back this notion up. There's a big part of the gay scene that's so accepting of the leather, kink, and fetish scenes, which makes it more accessible. How many of us have seen leather pups, Daddies, and Doms at pride each year? I saw at least three very good bois being walked on their leads down Hockley at Nottingham Pride, openly and proudly. I watched as one interacted with a young girl who pointed at him, delighted. His owner looked on proudly.

My own experiences with queer BDSM are minimal. When I came out, I was terrified. I cast my mind back to that time and feel sorry for myself. It's like losing your virginity all over again. I had to figure out where to put my hands, what to do with myself, and what the rules were. Were there even any rules? No one tells you how to date when you come out, and it's only then that you realise how gendered the rules of dating are. I'm supposed to wait for the guy to call, I'm meant to let the guy pay or open doors for me. So much of my time has been spent figuring out this new type of sex that I didn't stop to think about my interests in kinkier sex. It wasn't that I thought girls couldn't be kinky; I knew plenty of women who were into leather not lace, but I had to get the fundamentals right first.

I had sex with women in college despite labelling it as "just good fun." I had threesomes with my male partners where I felt it wasn't queer sex, because it was something we were doing together as a couple. I still told myself that even after one male partner walked out because he felt I was too interested in the girl we were joined with. It was a good ten minutes before I noticed he had gone.

Eventually I got more confidence, and it became harder to lie about what I was doing. I craved having an actual relationship with these women instead of the odd encounter where I could find it. When I met R, our relationship was steady, and I felt open enough to try new things with her, like strap-ons.

So we decided to purchase our first together. Making the mistake that a lot of people do, I overestimated the size I needed. "There is so much choice," I exclaimed while scrolling through pages of dildo attachments. "Am I a nine or a ten-inch person?" I mused out loud. As I don't do maths very well, I was struggling to understand the difference between an inch or centimetre. I finally found one that looked normal and clicked purchase.

When it arrived, I saw instantly the mistake I had made. First of all, the thing looked like a penis. I had been successfully running away from dicks at this stage, so I wasn't best pleased to have one with raised plastic veins in my house. I now see why there's a trend towards smooth non-human looking toys in bright colours, which would have been far preferable to what I'd ordered. I also saw the size.

We gave it our best try and despite my efforts, combined with a strong lube, we only used it once. My eyes watered at our attempt to even get it halfway in, so we gave up. It remains locked away in my drawer even now. I found that dominance or control didn't come naturally to our sex life either. R was too sweet to want to be nasty to me even though I would have allowed it. If it's not your thing or in your nature, then don't force it. I'm lucky that it's not a deal-breaker for me.

I hadn't drawn parallels between my ADHD and my need to be dominated. I don't need it all the time, but I do like it at certain times. This tends to be when my life is a bit more chaotic and I'm feeling overwhelmed. During the pandemic, I was trapped in the house I had bought, I had split from the girl I was going to propose to, and my financial worries were suffocating me. House problems were consuming me as a first-time homeowner of a very old house. One problem led to another, and I was coping alone without a partner or family. So I turned to a bit of bondage with a date in order to counter the fact I was overwhelmed by what was happening around me.

When restrictions lifted enough for us to see at least one other household, I bubbled with someone who lived alone too. We were horrendously lonely as both of us were shut off from our families, and there was a silence in our homes that hadn't existed before. The sex and the BDSM elements were enough to keep me distracted, along with the chance to pretend that it didn't feel like the end of the world was happening around us. We could play pretend relationship with each other when we both knew it was just sex. It helped me to process the sadness I felt around my breakup with R, because I felt a bit desired and wanted despite the months of lockdown loneliness.

Gradually, the house needed fewer repairs, so I was more in control. Lockdown lifted a bit, and I got to see my family briefly. I felt the lightening of the lockdown and I was mentally able to handle things a bit more. I'd had enough time since my breakup that I recognised I was finally able to consider life as a single person. To do this, I needed a fresh start, and I didn't want to be with anyone.

Blogger Joy Asitflies raises a point in the piece

on her ADHD that I hadn't considered before. She says she is deeply attracted to the power exchange during submissive (sub) and dominant (dom) sex as an ADHD person because being an ADHD person is exhausting. "By far the most relevant part of my kinky identity when it comes to ADHD is the realisation that I am not just sexually submissive but also deeply drawn to power exchange, to handing over control of everyday aspects of my life to a dominant individual who is happy to take over that responsibility, for our mutual satisfaction."[48]

I agree.

Remembering to do things daily is exhausting when you're battling a brain that makes you think about things differently. It's not impossible to go against your ADHD and win, but it is tiring, because you have to use a lot of core energy to do it. I do it daily, as we all do, and get things done. I have to work that much harder than a neurotypical person, because I have to think of ways to get around my ADHD, and it doesn't come naturally. Once, a friend commented to my mother that she was amazed that I couldn't lock my front door without trying several times to get it right. My mother, well used to it, simply nodded and confirmed this was because of my neurodivergence. I couldn't process the sequence that I needed to lift the handle until it clicked, *then* I needed to turn the key, otherwise it was half locked. I didn't realise this was ADHD until my mother pointed it out to me. I can't put things in a row properly or get acronyms right without getting them the wrong way around first.

This gets even more exhausting when you realise you're attempting to look normal in front of other people. I spent a lifetime not asking for extra help in school, college, or work because I wanted to be like everyone else. I didn't realise this came at a cost of looking slightly odd, because people didn't realise my behaviour, which seemed out of the norm on occasion, was a result of ADHD, not my oddness. I also didn't know that I was working twice as hard to get assignments in, relationships started, friendships going, or navigate college life because of my neurodiversity. I feel desperately sorry for myself in those years where I needed help and wouldn't ask. At university or school, I didn't ask for extensions or say anything when I was called on and couldn't answer quickly enough. I became easily exhausted and frustrated.

This is known as the cost of passing.

Laura James discusses this in her book on autism, *Odd Girl Out* and how she felt burned out as a result. She interviewed the clinical psychologist Tony Attwood about what this means for autistic people. "The cost of passing, it is essentially exhaustion brought on from the extra strain of someone pretending to be something that one is not." Tony Attwood summed it up well for me, telling me, "People with Aspergers or autism expend a huge amount of mental energy each day coping with socialising, anxiety, change, sensory sensitivity, daily living skills, and so on. So they are actually expending more mental energy. Think of it as an energy bank account. They are withdrawing so much energy throughout the day just by surviving."[49]

I hadn't considered that BDSM might be another way in which I cope as an ADHD person. I'm tired constantly, so if you offer me a way to easily switch my brain off, then I'll take it. I suspect this is also why ADHD people can abuse alcohol and drugs at much higher rates than our neurotypical counterparts.

I find this confirmed on Reddit as well. For my sins, I hate checking with Reddit but some nights when I can't sleep, I scroll through posts about relationship breakdowns, cannabis law reform (my work), and people asking if they're assholes for some thing or other they did. A post stated, "My partner has ADHD and he's the sub. I 100% believe that it helps him switch off from things (as is the case for most kinksters). I would say to all those on either side of the handcuffs that aftercare is probably even more important. With the emotional regulation issues, the sub/top drop can be intense sometimes."

Other comments jump out at me immediately confirming this.

Another Reddit person writes, "Vanilla is under-stimulating and frustrating to me. I seek out better experiences all the time and don't hold back. As a submissive ADHD person, I get off on being told what to do. I guess BDSM provides the external reinforcement/structure/stimulation I crave."[50]

I went back to the ADHD group I'd set up and steered away from Reddit before I lost my sanity. I wanted to see if any of the others liked the idea of BDSM for helping with the exhaustion of ADHD. I asked Emily, a twenty-four-year-old bi-curious ADHD person, and she said, "I dabble in BDSM as a switch, although I do prefer being in submissive roles since I don't have to think as much about things."[51]

The downside to checking social media is that I see some things I don't want to see. The internet is a cesspool of weirdos at the best of times. I wasn't quite prepared for the outpouring of anger, grief, and pain I found on a forum dedicated to ADHD partners, where neurotypical folk go to bitch about their partners. Some of it is badly needed and cleansing for people who love ADHD people but are at the end of their tether. There are only so many times you can see the same mistakes being made over and over before you need a place to rant. This, seemingly, is the place to go for that. Some of the comments fall directly into the mean and frankly, anti-neurodiversity categories, which wasn't pleasant to experience. It did confirm why writing this book was important. We need to see ourselves in books, forums, messages, and posts so we can feel less alone. Visibility is important for all communities and the ADHD one is no exception. Handle with care, and you can get a valuable insight into how neurotypical people can experience loving ADHD people.

I did notice a pattern with those who I interviewed in that almost everyone who described BDSM as being a regular thing for them were queer. I found a spectrum of sexuality attached to the descriptions of BDSM from pansexual to lesbian to bi-curious. I started to wonder if LGBT+ people were more inclined for kinky sex as it seems less odd to us. We're so used to being othered because of our sexuality that we don't see non-vanilla sex as unusual. I know that working in a sex shop for two years definitely means I don't see metal chastity belts, spikes, or leather harnesses as odd. Although I did blink when I saw my first PVC piss mat hanging up at the sex shop I worked at when I came in to start my shift one day.

NeuroQueer: A Neurodivergent Guide   157

Being Queer and Over Here

Ireland decriminalised homosexuality in 1993, when I was eight. I don't remember it happening because we didn't know any gays it would have affected. The irony of this is that of course we did, but no one was publicly out for obvious reasons. I was so sheltered. I still remember when I met my first friend from a broken home who had been through divorce, which had only been legal since 1997. These things were spoken about quietly in gossipy, hushed tones at Mass or in the shop, but never out loud or in public. When I realised I was queer, I simply kept quiet. I remember being attracted to a girl in my class when I was about twelve. I didn't know why I was looking at her in this new light, and it was confusing. I didn't know you were allowed to have feelings like that. No one spoke about being gay or what LGBT+ might be. My female friends all talked about boys and didn't seem interested in girls.

In part of the culture of silence, there is a subsection that could be called faux tolerance. We only made gay marriage legal in 2015 but prior to that, we had a wealth of gay bars around the country and a drag queen on national telly playing bingo. The country had tolerated LGBT+ people until it came to gays or transgender people screaming for rights. You can be you, but don't get too loud was the message. It was another strange form of homo/transphobia. Now that we have gay marriage, visible gay bars, and celebrity LGBT+ people, we are left with the same faux tolerance that now has a violent edge to it. A wave of attacks and murders of LGBT+ people are proof that even though we fought for our rights, we are still not fully accepted by everyone even today.

I asked Shar how they felt about the culture of silence around queerness and ADHD in Ireland.

"Anything that's outside the norm of expectations, we get caught in this paradox of attempted tolerance where it's like, we are totally fine with it, but we don't want to hear about it. We don't want to hear about it, see it, or support it. It's like that old-school homophobia where it is like, you can be as gay as you want, but don't do it in my face."

They added, "It can be incredibly frustrating when you are outside of that mould. You all have the same homework, same schoolbook, and do the same thing. So much of my experience with learning about my neurodiversity is so ingrained in my queer identity, because it's the same self-realisation and coming out. You never have to stop coming out and explaining about it. You deal with society's assumptions every day. Anytime you access healthcare, you nearly have to go in as an educator rather than a patient."

I came across an article by the paediatric neuropsychologist John Strang whose work focuses on gender, sexuality, and autism. The article, posted on Spectrum, an autism news and research site, *Why We Need to Respect Sexual Orientation, Gender Diversity in Autism*, speaks about the lack of LGBT+ autistic representation.

"However, emerging evidence suggests that autistic people are more likely to identify outside of conventional genders and sexualities than the general population is. The reasons for this are unclear, and they need to be studied. An international study published earlier this year revealed that nearly 70% of autistic respondents identify as non-heterosexual—more than double the rate in the general population. And a large Swedish study this year found that individuals with self-reported autistic traits are more likely than their peers to describe themselves either as bisexual or as not conforming to the labels of heterosexual, homosexual, or bisexual."[52]

Thing is, ADHD had already othered me when teachers started to treat me differently after my diagnosis. My mother took me to specialists, and I took different medications which my classmates weren't aware of. They were aware I was a bit quirky, and the teachers were reacting to my ADHD and schoolwork struggles. This had manifested in my being terrible at maths and withdrawn during languages. I wasn't cast out of the group in my primary school, but they knew I wasn't the same as them. I didn't want to stand out or be different, but I had no choice. Physically, I towered over others as a taller than average child with white-blond hair, and mentally I wasn't the same either. I've wondered since if never being inside the norm has meant I fell into subcultures my whole life. I'm so used to being on the outside that I can't consider life as an insider.

I became Goth, listened to metal, came out as queer, took part in BDSM. That's four different outsider cultures and minority groups right there. I take pride in my life as it is now. It has led me to some interesting experiences, and I've met some amazing people who are drag queens, sex workers, and artists. Really, you're never a complete outsider, because there is always a subculture group you just haven't met yet.

Sari Solden and Michelle Frank discuss

that ADHD people aren't purposely trying
to be different. "Women with ADHD are not
nonconformists out of choice; rather we have little
choice but to deviate from typical roles and social
norms due to our brain-based differences. Some
of us long to display more traditional gendered
behaviours, while others long to break the mould.
Women with ADHD, however, don't have as much
freedom in making the choice to depart, to stand
out, to be visibly divergent from the norm. This
conflict can be subtle, but it is deep, pervasive, and
not made out of an intentional life choice."[53]

Knowing you're different as an adult is one thing,
but it feels awful as a kid. You don't know that
you're going to have a much better and richer life
for it at that stage. In the grand tradition of school
kids who are confronted with a child that doesn't fit
their idea of normal, I was bullied as a result.

The book on radical ADHD for women also
states that, "Women with ADHD grow up
knowing viscerally that they are different. This is
compounded for women of colour, those who have
a physical disability or difference, those who identify
as LGBTQ, those of lower socioeconomic status, or
those who otherwise experience daily obstacles and
oppression for any number of differences—visible or
invisible."[54]

The authors consider that women silently
internalise that being different is wrong. We see
the standards set by neurodivergent folk and blame
ourselves for not measuring up. "During the course
of our lifetime, we as women with ADHD learn
through various channels that the way we think,
work, speak, relate, and act does not match up with
the preferred way of being in the world."[55]

The internalised shame we can feel as a result of being an ADHD woman reminds me of the shame described by Alan Downs in book on gay shame, *The Velvet Rage: Overcoming the Pain of Growing Up Gay in a Straight Man's World.* I remember reading it as someone struggling to come out and thinking, imagine being an out queer person but internally feeling all this shame for it. "So as mere children, years before we would have sex for the first time with a man, we had suffered rejection by our peers, emotional neglect from our fathers, and overcompensating protection from our mothers. We survived by learning to conform to the expectations of others at a time in our development when we should have been learning to follow in our own internal promptings."[56]

Thanks to the messages of silence, faux tolerance, and the teachings of Catholic Ireland, I internalised a lot of shame for both my queerness and my ADHD.

ADHD Time

Another area where I feel a lot of shame thanks to my ADHD is when something is so much harder for my neurodivergent brain than it should be. I've lost track of the number of times that simple tasks have taken me twice as long as they should because I haven't factored in my ADHD.

This is something I've seen within disability studies, and it's very true of ADHD too. Non-disabled people may consider that it takes twenty minutes to walk to the shop and back to get milk. This is based on the assumption that we have no physical factors to take into account. We can get up and go, then come back with no interruptions or considerations. To do so with a wheelchair, or crutches, or other disability means a totally different time frame and other needs to take into account. This is the same for those with chronic pain, and it may mean a different level of exhaustion too.

I found a crossover on this on the ADHD website, *ADDitude*. "How Long Does It Really Take? Time yourself on frequently travelled routes. You may be surprised to find that your ten-minute trip to the grocery store really takes twenty minutes. Stop underestimating your transit time. If you're planning a trip you've never made before, look up the route on an online service like Google Maps to find out how long the trip will take. If you'll be traveling during rush hour, add an extra 20% to your estimate."[57]

This is a fact, and it's solid advice.

I recently experienced this when on the way to the dentist, and I lost my wallet. "Where is it?" I panicked out loud, throwing my entire house into disarray. I had allowed twenty minutes to get out of the house and to the tram to get to the dentist across town in a pandemic. I *hadn't* planned to misplace my bank cards. I ripped the house a new one while searching for it, feeling utterly panicked as time ran out to catch the tram. Eventually I found the cards in the pocket of a jacket I rarely used and called an Uber to get me across town sharpish. I knew I hadn't seen the cards for a while, but it hadn't occurred to me that I needed to track them down in order to make that small window of time I had allotted. I can feel the waves of neurotypical folk rolling their eyes and thinking, "Big deal. I lose shit on occasion." The problem is that we do things like this all the time, we're powerless to change how our brain works, and it's seriously distressing to have it happen. I also failed to take into account that my brain would have issues figuring out the door lock sequence which also slowed me down.

I got into the Uber and then felt ashamed and upset that I had done this to myself, knowing I'm ADHD. No one ever told me about ADHD time though. No one was there to say, "Hey, listen, be kind to yourself. This is how your brain works. Give yourself extra time because of the unique way you move through life." I sat in the back of the taxi feeling shame, embarrassment, and worry that my new housemate thought I was crazy for stomping around. It's not just the losing things like this; it's also the absolute terror of having to find my way across trains and buses, and having to navigate routes. I have genuine panic attacks over it.

One Size Doesn't Fit All

During this research, I came across a point of view on social media that grabbed my attention. It talks about concentration and subs. A poster who identified as an ADHD Dom said in 2016, "I don't understand how someone with ADHD is supposed to enjoy things like bondage and holding positions. I get how the masochistic stuff isn't really affected by ADHD, but the whole sitting still thing seems like torture, and not in the hot way. Maybe I'm just not wired to enjoy that kink as a sub? (I'm a Dom with ADHD)."[58] The subs were quick to jump in and point out that hyperfocus can help us to engage for long periods of time. Surprisingly, I can remain focused when in a BDSM session as a submissive because

I'm engaged with it, but I struggle to sit still in the hairdressers. I can't switch this focus on or off when I want to, which is why ADHD gets a bad reputation for being about a lack of focus. Really, we just have to find the way to engage with what we're doing.

Someone linked the poster to a *FetLife* forum discussion on this very topic. The site, which focuses on fetish and kink, is one I've come across before. A Dom had written a piece about how to be mindful of ADHD in a submissive.

While most of it was nothing I hadn't considered before, there was one section that caught my eye about time. I agree that I think some activities take longer with ADHD and that we all experience time differently. But I hadn't thought about the long stretches of time that I experience hyperfocus and subsequently missing time periods. It's what I took to referring to as ADHD blackout.

On a forum in the deepest, darkest part of the internet, a conversation took place on ADHD, time, and kink. I'll keep it vague to avoid any identification.

One person posted, "They will experience what is known as hyperfocus from time to time, and this can often cause time warps. This is where we get in a 'zone' where we are really into doing whatever it is we are doing. It can be like the rest of the world does not exist; it may be hard to get the attention of a person experiencing this. Unfortunately, when this happens and what activity it happens to can't really be controlled at all. The time warp effect mentioned is because time can pass extremely quickly for that person while it is happening."[59]

So this explains how I can have BDSM sex for hours, but I can't sit still at a hairdressers. When I have BDSM sex, I know it's rare and I've signed up for it. I think my biggest challenge will be combining my hyperfocus with my hyposexuality because if I'm honest, I haven't learned how to do that yet. As the above point stresses, we can't control when this hyperfocus happens. If we did, then ADHD folk would make the most amazing employees, and we'd live in spotless houses. I know that my hyperfocus can also manifest with people where I become obsessive, but what goes up must also come down. I switch off, creating another reason not to have sex.

God, ADHD and sex is so complicated.

Chapter Seven
Me, Myself, and I:
Solo Sex and the Art of Kindness

"Come on, it'll be fun," I whined. "I never get to do anything like this. Do it for me? Please?" I pulled on my partner's arm like a small child asking to go into a toy shop when in reality, I'm a fully grown person asking for permission to go look at dildos.

I was performing the age-old ritual of trying to drag a grown man into a shop. Not just any shop but *insert name of generic high street sex shop here.* I'd wanted to go in for ages but had never had the guts to do it. I also lived in the schticks so this was the only time I'd been in the city without my parents. It may not have been the raciest sex shop that the city of Cork has to offer now but when I was seventeen, there weren't a lot of options. It was also the only one I suspected won't ask me to leave for being under-age.

It was Saturday morning, and I was stood outside the store, gazing in the window. I'd been dying to get a vibrator for multiple reasons but mainly because all the magazines and TV shows told me that I was going to LOVE it.

I was going through the worst part of a rebellious phase of piercing bits, dying my hair, and shouting at my mother, so this was another way I could prove how painfully cool I was. I'd be the first person in the parish to own one (yeah, right).

I was correct in assuming the shop wouldn't kick me out as the staff eyed me with great boredom.

I looked like I was too young to have any decent money to spend, so I was no good to their high targets. I walked up and down the aisle looking at the rows of brightly coloured dildos with ridiculous names. There were whips near fluffy, more delicate-looking items, and paddles on the faux-leather-look wallpaper. I learn later in life that I'll have to go to a specialist store to see the really intense stuff. But back then, the most outrageous thing under the counter was poppers. I also learn later on when I worked in this same store that you can get staff discount on the poppers, which I took to doing every Friday night.

I had the bored expression of a seventeen-year-old who thinks themselves world-wise but in reality knew nothing.

The dildos were in the centre of the store, so I headed there. It was an overwhelming display of glitter, girth, and buttons. Some even had their own balls and veins. I couldn't work out what size was the right for me, so I selected what seemed like a medium compromise. By which, I mean I plumped for a nine-inch purple number that I might need those poppers for. The "thing," as I called it, had a long, purple glitter shaft with rotating balls and a head that looked like a realistic penis. A smaller, rabbit-shaped lump of plastic protruded from the side of it. The staff were still ignoring me as I slid it across the counter. I needed advice, but my Irish Catholic self wouldn't ask someone. I might actually have died of embarrassment if they'd spoken to me.

I was gutted when the vibrator didn't work for me.

When I finally reached the age of twenty-one, I started working in the same high street sex store (that will remain nameless) to sell vibrators. I started to appreciate that they're not all made equal. Some are made for lesbians, some are for heterosexual folk, and most are *not* made for neurodivergent people. As I didn't see anything that would work for me on sale anywhere, I assumed it was my fault. I just happened to have the one body that vibrators don't work for. I internalised that it was me at fault, not the industry itself that had a problem.

Fast forwarding to my own sex shop work experience and one day, I was slapping price tags on some anal beads, as you do. I heard a voice at the counter ask, "Excuse me, do you have any catalogues?"

"Sure we do. How many would you like?" I sighed, not looking up from the beads. After all, our catalogues are famous, free masturbation material for people who won't purchase porn. Keep in mind this is pre-internet porn days.

"Would thirty be okay?"

Okay, so now I looked up because even the most outrageous of the customers had only ever tried to take five at the same time.

She looked sheepishly at me. "I run a sex workshop for disabled people, and we want to talk to the group about sex toys."

I handed her as many as she could fit in her tote bag.

It had embarrassingly never occurred to me until then that some people need things like this. I hadn't even figured out at that stage that I, as a neurodivergent person, also needed things like this so it wasn't surprising. I was twenty-one and I also thought a bottle of Buckfast was an acceptable dinner.

I am not alone in this. I read Emma Shepard's PhD thesis, *Kinked and Crippled: Disabled BDSM Practitioners' Experiences and Embodiments of Pain*, which touches on this as she talked about working in a sex shop while struggling with fibromyalgia, where she was constantly asked for accessible sex toys. It wasn't just sex toys, it was also access to the kink community.

"I used to work in a sex shop. I always hasten to tell people that it was a nice sex shop, with lovely, friendly, not-creepy customers, and I had taken my mother in there for tea and cake. These things are true, but I paid the bills by selling sex toys and pornography to people. Two things came up in those six months: firstly, inquiries as to whether the shop stocked disability porn. Secondly: disabled people asking for advice from 'Is this lubricant safe for sensitive skin' to 'Where's a good wheelchair-accessible sex club?' Disability porn was one of many niche interests the shop's customers came looking for, and it was rather difficult to find. The latter was more interesting, and after looking around and finding a small—but thorough—amount of advice for disabled people in heterosexual relationships wishing to insert tab A into slot B in a mutually gratifying manner, I realised there was not much around that discussed sex—or sexuality—more broadly, more queerly."[60]

The Toy Shop

Going back to my own sex shop years, I wanted to get stuck into the research of finding *The Very Best Toy Ever* as soon as I could. I had a staff discount, so I was able to buy a different vibrator nearly every month. Soon I had more anal beads, rotating shafts, and fancy lubes than I knew what to do with.

I bought a small bullet vibrator one day that had a long wire connected to a chunky white box. It was called the iGasm, and it clipped into your iPod so that you could listen to music and vibe in time to it.

At this stage, I lived in student accommodation connected to the art college. It was the usual, crowded student flats where there were a lot of doors being slammed, parties, and loud voices. It was virtually impossible to switch off from the ever-present sound of people coming and going in the house. The iGasm offered me a way to get out of my head, out of my student accommodation, and into an experience.

So, like all good products that I learned to love, it was taken off the market shortly after. Apple caught on the catch name of the product and issued a "Dear god, please stop it, you perverts" cease and desist letter, which the company willingly obeyed.

I eventually left sex shop work and took a big break from sex-everything. While I still had sex, I was so over the idea of investing in it. I had become bored by the very idea of the sex I saw sold to me. I had a bulging bag of dildos left over from my sex toy sales discount, so I wasn't exactly short of things to mount.

I didn't go into another sex shop actively looking for products for about ten years after that. One day, a partner and I visited a small town's sex store on the hunt for something to take camping with us. The brightly coloured boxes and bored staff were the same old, same old. But a huge digital revolution in dildos had taken place. The apps, Bluetooth, and LED lights replaced chunky plastic, big buttons, and wires. I felt as if I was that teenager looking for a new toy all over again. "This can connect to our phones so we can monitor our orgasms," my ex shouted, sounding impressed while she waved the box at me. A small, C-shaped vibrator that curved around our bodies and rested on our clitoris with the option to be paired to a phone was purchased and just like that, I had entered sex tech with no help, no professional advice, and no idea what I was doing. I was so overwhelmed by the choice and the flashing buttons.

I turned to my ADHD group to ask about sex toys and what their experiences had been. Immediately a few responses jumped out at me.

Emily, a twenty-four-year-old woman who describes herself as bi-curious said, "Some sex toys are way too distracting. My partner got this rubber vibrator thing on a little ring that goes around his dick, and I absolutely hated the thing. I think after a minute of me being way too focused on whether it was perfectly lined up and readjusting it, I finally told him it had to go. Not all sex toys distract me, but this one did. I do love a good vibrator though but a real one, not some gimmicky vibrating cock ring from the drug store."

Anne, twenty-four, is in a relationship with another ADHD woman. She says that sex toys help to keep them going despite feeling tired, although she's unsure if her tiredness is due to ADHD or her fibromyalgia. "Yes, sometimes they do help. I think that might be due to the fact that after a while, my girlfriend gets tired or worn out, as do I, and as we all do during sex. Whereas toys can just keep going without interruption or having to take breaks."

I decided I needed to call in the professionals if

I was going to talk about sex toy design. I spoke to Raven Faber of EngErotics over Zoom one snow-filled January afternoon. Raven isn't just a sex toy designer but also a talented engineer who chose to go into the sex tech and CBD industries.

We started with a discussion on how sex toys could be adapted, and often are, for physical disabilities. "There are a number of considerations to design anything for different abilities—it has to be about access on some level," Raven said. "In day to day, in everything we use, we see wheelchair ramps, Braille on buttons, and closed captioning, and all of these are tools to make things accessible for people who are not able-bodied."

She added that: "When it comes to designing products, not just sex products, but all products, it needs to be designed in a way that's accessible for disability or people with physical challenges to use. It could be something that's easy to grip, like in *Grace and Frankie* on Netflix, they have a whole conversation around being old ladies, and we need this big vibrator with this handle that's easy to hold because of arthritis and things that develop with age. We have a client, and she loves this particular toy that she can slip between her fingers, so handle design can be a big deal.

"My experience with people who are neurodiverse is that I used to teach autistic and ADHD children how to swim, as I used to be a lifeguard. We had a lot of kids who had issues with getting water in or on their ears. I started to notice that texture was a big deal, [and] noise, or routine. Things have to be done like this as they know the routine, and it's about predictability."

This idea of predictability is huge. I am a terror

for being upset when my routine changes, and the slightest change can throw me into a tailspin of anxious doom. I'm happiest when I'm in control of my environment. But I've never considered how this could affect my orgasms.

"In the context of sex device design, I would say that the texture of the toy is really important," Raven said. "You can't comfortably use something that feels yucky to you. I've had people tell me they can't stand the touch of smooth or bumpiness when toys are textured. So, do we need to have a vibrator that has interchangeable sleeves, or some way people can change the texture? Do we have a vibrator that takes the user through a routine that doesn't change? I would imagine this is really jarring if you accidentally hit a button. Visual stimulation too, as I know many people are over stimulated by the flashing LEDs that we see on the fancier things."

For all the bells and whistles, vibrators that could do everything for me bar make me a sandwich, I prefer a little click and off version. A tiny one that didn't allow me to get upset or overwhelmed by the things on offer. There's nothing fancy, but it gives me comfort when it comes to reliability. My ADHD is overwhelmed by the options of speed, apps, and lights to the point where my energy is gone before I've even used it.

One area I think does need improving is how sex store staff are educated and how to engage with neurodivergent folk. I mention my experiences, or lack of them, to Raven.

"We've come a long way, and the industry has progressed in leaps and bounds, but we still have a long way to go," she said. "If I was an associate in a brick-and-mortar store and someone neurodiverse came in looking for something, then you need to be very intentional with your recommendations. You need to ask certain questions so you can recommend appropriate products, but you need to know about neurodiversity and have empathy. So ask about texture, stimulus, light, noise, or is it a combination of these things?"

It suddenly dawns on me that I've missed the massive comparison between sex shopping and foundation shopping. Bear with me on this one.

When I worked in makeup artistry, I sold foundations that came in over sixty-seven shades and fifteen different formulas. After a while, I could tell a foundation shade as it walked in the door. However, the shade I may have been able to diagnose, but I could never tell how much coverage a person wanted or how their skin was beneath it. So, I would need to ask.

These are all very serious considerations in makeup world. If you put a light coverage, water-based foundation on someone who likes a Kardashian makeup effect, then you're creating a refund situation, if they even invest at all. So my training in makeup taught me to ask open-ended questions designed to get people talking. "What is your skin like?" I would ask while holding a brush to their face. "What coverage do you like?" or "How would you like your skin to look?"

The person would normally give me enough information to recommend a product that fit their skin. Even with that, we would place three swatches on their cheek, get them to feel different formulas and try on one all over the face before we selected one. I realised I had never had a sex shop staff member approach me like this or ask me these questions, yet this product was going inside me.

Vibrators should be sold like makeup. They aren't though.

I decided to test this theory in the wild. There was a huge problem though; we were in the middle of a third lockdown, which meant I couldn't get a haircut, let alone something for the weekend for my vagina. Only one thing for it, I was going to have to take this show on the virtual road.

I googled adult products or adult toys for ADHD, autism, or neurodiversity. I was curious to see what came up and if it was relevant or not. My search returned nothing but sensory toys for ADHD and autistic children.

My first stop was the internet's biggest online sex store, and I'm guessing you know the one I'm referring to if you've ever done this search yourself. I've bought from them before, but I'd never actually spoken to the store for help. I decided to hit the button marked LIVE CHAT.

A chatbot pops up perkily. "Hi! I can help with most questions about *INSERT HIGH STREET STORE NAME HERE*. (Even though I'm not a real person!) Please enter your question below."

Now I'm not stupid; I know that a chatbot won't have the meaning of life, but surely, it could tell me to wait until an advisor was free. After all, my heating provider's chatbot does that. I typed back, "I need some recommendations on sex toys that would suit an ADHD person."

The chatbot snapped back instantly. "We have a large selection of sex toys for males, which you can browse here: Http…"

Erm, did you just assume because I wrote ADHD that I need male sex toys?

I was a bit confused. I needed tech support for the tech support. My second attempt gave me the same answer which wasn't a great look for the company.

The next day I tried again at more reasonable human hours when I suspected I'd have more luck reaching an actual person. I spoke to a real-life human called Emily who admitted to never having had the question of sex toys for ADHD people before. Her suggestions weren't bad though, once I explained a bit more about what I needed. I also outed myself as queer fairly early on, so I didn't have to go through the whole hetero expectation.

Her first questions were open ones that invited me to give more information into what vibrator would suit me. "Do you have a budget you would like to stick to? Do you know what kind of stimulation you're looking for?" she asked me through the chat. After a bit of discussion, she suggested a range of vibrators. They were simple on and off options with low tech, so I couldn't get overwhelmed, and I noticed that, without asking, she had selected ones that aren't penis shaped. Nice touch, Emily, I thought as I mentally scored her Brownie points for appealing to my anti-dick vibrator stance.

While the website didn't have anything like the iGasm, I don't blame it, as few companies appear to be offering these options now. Emily suggested a simple rechargeable clitoral vibrator. On first glance, it was simple and didn't need an app, which appealed to me. It's click and go. However, I realised that it did have a handy function for recording your preferred mode, which was also soothing to me and my desire for reliability and routine.

Emily admitted that they needed more training in suggesting things for neurodiverse folk, but I had to admit that her advice had been decent enough, and her suggestions were solid. I think a lot of that comes down to us getting vocal and asking for help. I would never have approached someone before to talk about what I need from a vibrator, despite this being my literal job all those years ago. Sex shop staff aren't just workers in a store but could be educators with a bit of rethinking.

In her book on vibrators, *Vibrator Nation*, Lynn Comella discusses how early women's sex shops were exactly this: a space to get educated. She tells the history of different US sex shops such as Babeland and its creator Carrie Schrader. "While Schrader was helping her [a customer] choose a vibrator, she had a powerful realisation: this woman trusted Schrader to give her the information she needed to make a profound change in her life. She came to believe that the interactions Babeland enabled between sales staff and customers could be transformative, and that every time someone walked through the business's doors seeking more pleasure in her or his sex life, it was, Schrader claimed, 'One small revolution.' Babeland's ability to positively impact people's lives, she felt, was boundless."[61]

The book charts the growth of education-led, safe spaces that were adult stores from the 1970s to the early '00s, before the internet and profitability became an issue. It seems unthinkable reading this today that we're in a situation where customers are ignored, the default sex shop setting is heterosexual, and staff aren't educated on how to deal with diversity. How have we gone backwards?

What Changed and Where Are We Now?

I worked in retail for ten years for some sex and some not so sex stores. The issue is not always staff but rather, the conditions. Working in one of the biggest sex shops in Ireland, I was given a financial target, a product target, and told to hop to it. If my target wasn't met then I would be called in, called out, and let go. The store also prioritised a certain toy over the others, as it had designed and made a fortune on it. If my target was to sell five of these a day to avoid losing my job, then I aimed towards that instead of suggesting another product that might be better suited.

Simply put, I didn't have time to talk to people about what they needed, and I wasn't incentivised to care either. This does (and yet doesn't) make me a bad employee, but it does mean that I was carrying on the grand tradition of selling people useless vibrators for a lot of money.

However, Lynn Comella made the point that the media and the internet have brought a more normalised and sanitary sex shop experience, as did more mainstream stores developing on the original idea of collectives and DIY spaces to create a more high street-friendly, albeit bland, version. An experience that started with those '70s feminist and queer sex stores but took decades to mature. "These cultural shifts did not happen overnight. The increasing availability of sex toys and the growth of the women's market are the results of decades worth of efforts on the part of feminist retailers, manufacturers, and educators to make sexual products more responsible—and therefore more acceptable to segments of Middle America that previously would never have dreamed of venturing into an adult store."[62]

With the high street-ification of sex shops came targets that had nothing to do with women. As a result, staff are often pressured to make money, not improve masturbation. Staff are often underpaid, overworked, and under pressure.

Again, *Vibrator Nation* comments on this: "Feminist retailers and staff must navigate commercial imperatives that are not always in sync with their progressive ideals or more inclusive versions of feminism and queer politics."[63]

As she highlights, there is a comfortable line between money and education. This is what I felt when my employer needed to make rent on the space so asked me to sell a €100 dildo to a woman who needs a €10 clitoral stimulator. It is the worst feeling, but as a minimum wage worker on the bottom rung of the ladder who also needs to pay rent, I ain't got much choice.

While companies are starting to ask what they can do for different communities, it has taken a long time to get going on this. As Jennie Williams from Love Lounge put it to me, everyone will be disabled at some point in their lives. If you consider this, then the area of carefully considered toy design has the capacity to make serious bank for a company. Yet so many companies remain sceptical, scared, or not bothered about catering for this percentage of the population.

"There isn't a lot of diversity in the sex industry. Especially in the media, when people talk about sex and disability, it tends to be in terms of disability and sex work that someone has got to pay to have sex. But actually, we are missing out on the basics that most of us have learned about sex by having sex with ourselves. It was about exploring your body through masturbation. If you haven't got the ability to do that, like with dexterity for example, then that's a really big deal," Jennie said. "We always say that not-disabled people are not yet disabled. The reality is, we're all going to be disabled at some point in our lives. Hopefully for most people, that's not until we are older. Our bodies change all the time, so we should be always thinking about our future selves and how the sex industry can reflect us."

She warns against the inclusiveness feeling forced, which is something that I worry about too. I worry that the industry, in a hurry to provide for a gap in the market, is in danger of being either useless or offensive. "It should feel natural and be inclusive rather than going, this is specifically for disabled people or for people who are seemingly different or outside of the norm. It could just be that this is inclusive, and this is cool. Text messaging was originally invented for deaf people and now everyone texts. That's how it should be."

I've been asked a few times by people what constitutes a good adult toy for ADHD people. The thing is, we're all so different, and the research just isn't out there. If it is out there, then a lot of the time, it ignores the queer experiences of LGBT+ ADHD people. It's less about the best toy but rather, having a choice, being educated, and helped to find what works for us as neurodiverse people and also, what we need it for.

I strongly suggest that sex toy designers look at the different ways they can help the experience of masturbation for neurodivergent folk. This could be a vibrator that connects to your Spotify to vibe in time to the music. What if it came with changeable sleeves in a number of textures, where you can change one if you hate the feel? What if the vibrator came with a subscription to audio porn sites?

Oh, and batteries should be rechargeable, because I never remember to buy them and from an environmental standpoint, that's important.

One area I'm curious about is the idea of fidget spinners for sexy time. I'm going somewhere with this concept, so hear me out. I wonder if you took the idea of a fidget spinner, which is something to hold in your hand to help direct your energy and take out nervous attention, would it help? I wonder what the sex equivalent of that is? I know that my first orgasm happened because I was able to have something to do with my free hand. I just have no idea what this looks like for this purpose. Fidget toys work for ADHD people, yet no one has wondered if this could work for sex toys. I think it's an interesting gap in the market which could prove to be incredibly useful.

I think keeping it simple is key. I can cope with an app set-up if it's easy or doesn't get too confusing. It could even just connect to your Bluetooth headphones. What if you could hit a button to store your favourite mode? Keep the modes simple too because having a lot of options can be full on.

Here's another suggestion. Queerify your products. Instead of "Toys for her" or "Couples' toys," which veer towards hetero couples, accept that sometimes, men have vaginas and women can have a penis. Lynn Comella talks about the radical move to remove gender from vibrators in *Vibrator Nation*. "Push[ing] past limits that don't really need to be there. In this sense, the act of queering is about disassembling normative ideas about the relationship between gender, sexuality, and bodies, and creating alternative configurations and possibilities—what we think of as queer rearticulations."[64]

"Don't let what a toy is intended for stop you from thinking about all the different ways it can be used. Dayes (a sex store worker) began to queer sex toys by not attaching products to a specific practise or gender. For example, male/female couples can use a vibrating cock ring during intercourse, but a cock ring can also be placed on a dildo or around a finger and used for manual stimulation of any number of body parts by people of any gender."[65]

I'd also like to suggest that staff need to be educated. I don't expect them to be a world of information about what defines ADHD traits but encouraging them to get to know how sex looks for people would be amazing. Questions like, what would make it easier for you, what problems do you face, with vibrators/etc., that you have had before? Work with the person to come to an idea of what could work for them.

Porn

I never thought in a million years that I would write about how porn has helped me. I think we don't give it enough credit, but we give it plenty of criticism, which we need to.

Here are some truths about porn:

Porn is hilarious.

It's valid work.

It's used by women to get off.

It's used by ADHD people to get off.
It can be dark and dangerous at times.
It can be dark and dangerous and illegal at times.
But used legally and ethically, it can be really helpful.

I'm a big believer that sex work is valid work, but it needs to be safe work. A lot of the porn we consume online simply isn't safe for those working in the industry, and we have no way to check that it is. We just log in and hope for the best. We expect that the site has done enough checks, and those involved have signed enough papers to ensure that their employees are consenting adults.

While I wasn't new to porn in my thirties, I was new to how it could help me masturbate. I don't often masturbate in a fancy way, where I take time out to plan out a sexy night in. I often have half an hour where I feel slightly less tired than normal and an empty house. When you are ADHD, planning your time isn't really the easiest task, which all of the self-help books tell you to do. While I wrote about hyposexuality making life difficult because I avoid sex with a partner, it can also make me avoid masturbation too. I get tired of trying to herd my mind into a space where I feel sexy and not focused on work or finances. This is again where having a vibrator comes in handy, because it's so much easier to help you stay on track.

I sort of got the wrong idea about masturbation from an early age. I wasn't ashamed of it, but I suspected I was doing it all wrong. On TV, women masturbate on their back while slipping a hand down to their crotch and scream almost immediately. It absolutely did not occur to me that this was for the sake of the cameras until I was

an embarrassing age. I realised this when I saw
Chewing Gum in 2015, made by Michaela Coel. In
the program, her character masturbates by grinding
on a cushion while talking about the unrealistic state
of porn (fair) and getting turned on by the same
porn. This cushion-grinding was repeated in the
Netflix series *You* in 2018 when the character Becks
used a cushion in her living room to masturbate.

I hadn't seen women masturbate like this until
I actually saw women do it on TV. It's not how all
women masturbate—because otherwise a lot of
home furnishings would be destroyed—but I know
that's how I started.

Sex therapist Vanessa Marin, creator of Finishing
School, an online orgasm course for women, told
Bustle Magazine in 2019 that this method is more
normal than we think. "Grinding (of any kind) is
one of the most common female masturbation
techniques," Marin agrees. "Most women who use
this technique think that they're the only woman in
the world who masturbates in this way, so they're
always relieved to know that it's super common!
Most women started masturbating this way as
children, without fully realising what they were
doing."[66]

I am the last person to know this, apparently.
Glamour magazine followed this with a four-page
spread in their SS20 issue with Chrissy Teigen
on the cover. The magazine dove into the murky
world of masturbation and came back with some
surprising statistics from a readers' poll of over one
thousand women. An incredible 92% of the women
surveyed masturbated, with 79% viewing it as self-
care. In fact, 77% of these women viewed it as their
primary form of self-care, with 54% saying it was

good stress relief. What was interesting was that only 67% of women reach orgasm when they touch themselves.[67]

But what about ADHD folk? I refer to Ari Tuckman's book, *ADHD After Dark: Better Sex Life, Better Relationships.* Tuckman asked three thousand straight people, including men, about their masturbation habits. "For *both* genders, those with ADHD masturbated more than those without. When we look at the difference between the partners in the two types of couples, we again see that a woman who has ADHD is more likely to be similar to her non-ADHD male partner in her masturbation frequency, compared to the difference between a man with ADHD and his non-ADHD female partner."[68]

I had heard that ADHD people masturbate more often, and I worried about why this was so different for me. I know that my masturbation levels increased when I discovered ways of getting straight to it. In discovering porn and vibrators, I gave my mind a way to focus that meant I wasn't constantly getting distracted, then upset and frustrated.

Tuckman claims that there are four main reasons for a partner avoiding masturbation: "For women, both with and without ADHD, there were four barriers that were found to be related to how often they masturbated. For three of these barriers, the more they rated it as a barrier, the less they masturbated.

'I am disinterested in sex in general, not just with this partner.'

'I am too tired to have sex.'

'It can be difficult to switch gears from other demands and be sexual.'"[69]

All of these applied to my relationship with R. I was so disinterested in sex when we were together. I could go six months to a year without masturbation or sex in any form.

When I had solo sex unaided, it gave my brain a way to let in the distractions. "OMG DID YOU TURN THE OVEN OFF?" or "THE CRACK IN THE CEILING LOOKS NEW AND COULD BE DANGEROUS; MAKE SURE YOU LOOK AT IT THIS INSTANT."

When we split up, I moved into a very small home and rented out my second bedroom to a number of different housemates. The rooms were connected by a thin strip of wooden landing where *every* sound could be heard. I panicked frequently about the noise, but my biggest anxiety was around the idea that my vibrator would be heard. This meant I had to start listening to music fairly loudly.

It took some selection to find an album that wasn't intrusive or didn't change pace too often, but eventually I did. While selecting the music, I realised I wanted some visuals to go with it, which is when I started to use porn.

I'm not alone in enjoying porn, apparently. That *Glamour* survey revealed that 35% of those surveyed watch porn. While it's unclear how many women took part in the survey, that's not a small percentage.

ADHD people also enjoy porn. Going back to the Tuckman book again, he discovered people watch porn more often when they have ADHD. This translates to twenty-four times a year, or every 15.2 days compared to non-ADHD women who do it twelve times a year, every 30.4 days.

This is where the issue of ethical porn comes in. I feel okay about watching sex but not about the ethics of porn. How it's displayed is often horrific and distracting when you're looking for something to watch. It's not displayed in a way that is sensitive, sexy, or descriptive but rather a way that's designed for men and algorithms to pick up. Most of these sites aren't marketed at queer audiences or women and yet, we still use them.

A quick flick onto one site shows me exactly what I mean when I refer to off-putting content. *"Swingers defile redhead teen and her husband,"* shouts one title above a video of a terrifyingly young redhead.

I get that, "Queer couple make a lovely cup of tea and then have respectful sex on the cream sofa" isn't going to generate clicks, which is all that matters to most porn content creators. No content online matters without the clicks, likes, or validation that comes from high numbers engaging with it. Porn makers use those all-important keywords, which is why we've gotten to a situation where we have "Teen fuck fests" instead of anything normal sounding. Don't get me wrong, these keywords are driven by what men click on, so the blame isn't entirely on the SEO team.

The tide is turning, but it costs money. If you're willing to part with coin, then there are sites out there that can help. I started my research one lonely Friday night with a glass of wine in hand, ready for an education. My search brought me to Birmingham's first ethical porn festival, Bean Flicks, which combines films, discussions, and cock- or cunt-tails made by a mixologist. Yet another resource that I had to wait for lockdown to stop to access.

On a more indoor night in vibe, I found the Lust

Cinema by Erika Lust.[70] It aims to "challenge the porn industry standards by promoting the cinematic possibility of the medium, high quality storytelling, and a realistic representation of human sexuality and sex."

The site works by offering membership at different levels from $11.50 to $34.50 depending on how much access you'd like. I flicked through the titles. "Crushing on my bestie," said one calmly while two grown women look longingly at each other. "Quick before someone sees," urged another. There wasn't one questionable title on here, and it added to the experience.

I do want to raise one issue here; there is an uncomfortable balance to be struck. We have become all too familiar with getting our content, both sexual and non-sexual, for free. Sex workers in porn need to be paid and paid well to do what they do. However, there is also access to consider here as ADHD people can be in low paid jobs or not employed at all. A study from 2021 discovered that ADHD had a 17% lower income, more days of unemployment, and a higher likelihood of being on disability pension in comparison to the control group. This was higher for individuals who had co-morbid ADHD like me, where it combines with another condition such as ODD.[71]

As a cost-of-living crisis deepens around us, there is less and less spare cash for things like paid porn, which creates an ethical dilemma as we are pushed back into the cycle of free, yet questionable, content.

Another area that I hadn't considered before was the area of audio porn which has been gaining popularity in recent months. The concept is simple in that it's just the audio side without the visuals, leaving it all to your imagination. While there has been a huge increase in the numbers of women turning to all things audio, I have found as a non-binary person that this works for me too. There are a number of sites that allow you to really tailor your experience, such as *Quinn*, which allows you to pick male, female, or even non-binary voices and your interests. If you fancy a bit of heavy breathing or a story about a sexy situation read in a certain accent, then it's all yours to explore.

ADHD people, in particular women, have often been accused of being daydreamers. I know this is certainly true for me; I'm forever being told off for my head being elsewhere. However, this is one area where our daydreaming might actually come in handy. Also, it becomes very easy to put yourself into the action too.

So why not just listen to the sounds of porn? Well, there's no reason that you can't but again, it comes down to finding something that isn't just recorded with the male gaze, or in this case ears, in mind.

There are potential scientific reasons for this too, but you might have to give me a second and allow me a boiling hot take (or rather, a theory, no matter how batshit). There are schools of thought around music therapy and the ADHD brain. Some therapists argue that it can help to boost attention and focus while reducing hyperactivity. It's thought that the music can fire up the dopamine levels in the brain, which explains why I live on my Spotify account. But could it be the same for other sounds? This could be an interesting experiment to see how audio erotica, or porn, or even sex-free ASMR works on ADHD brains. This could also explain why the music-adjacent vibrator worked so well for me too.

In an article with *ADDitude* magazine, neurologic music therapist Patti Catalano explained how dopamine levels, our brains, and ADHD work with music. She also stressed that this could build up brain muscles over time for better functioning for kids.

"Research shows that pleasurable music increases dopamine levels in the brain. This neurotransmitter—responsible for regulating attention, working memory, and motivation—is in low supply in ADHD brains. "Music shares neural networks with other cognitive processes. Through brain imaging, we can see how music lights up the left and right lobes. The goal of music therapy is to build up those activated brain muscles over time to help overall function. Kids with ADHD attend to everything," Catalano says. "They are more sensitive to auditory stimulation and less able to tune things out."[72]

When it comes to sex with a partner, I found that the audio aspect has a huge role to play in grounding me in the experience, so there's a lot to be said for being a good listener. I discovered through accident, then repeated on purpose, that I like my partner's breathing and talking in my ear. It helps to ground me in the experience a bit more.

I've started to consider my environment a bit more. A weird side benefit of the shared accommodation I mentioned is the constant fear that someone is going to hear me. This has forced me to consider things like music, better and more silent toys, and also, while I'm at it, setting the lighting because I need the curtains closed. I have to find the right audio, the right image, or the right toy.

On the other hand, this means that the set-up needs to be just right, otherwise it's going to be a frustrating time. My brain can sometimes look anywhere for stimulation other than where I want it to. So I have to really want it to stay in the actual room. There were times pre-vibrators and porn where I just gave up. I needed the speed and focus that these things gave me.

Getting Educated

So when it came to learning about sex and masturbation, I had turned to magazines a lot as a teenager who was starting to get interested in sex.

My mother didn't want to talk about sex, bodies, or periods with me, so I got a lot of my education from these instead. I learned that if boys were mean to me then it usually meant they liked me. Which was fine, except I lived in rural West Cork and went to Catholic all girls' schools, and there were no boys to be mean to me. I devoured features about how you could make your own skincare, how texting could be an addiction, and how to know if a boy wanted to ask you out. I didn't know at that stage that I would be writing a lot of these things for a living later in life. I've advised readers on the same subjects I binged on as a child, only now it's "Are lip fillers addictive?" and "How can I tell if someone on Tinder wants to murder me and wear me as a skin suit?"

Sex, masturbation, and relationship advice was always the same in these magazines. Even today, when I turned to *Cosmopolitan* to see what they suggested, their main tips were laughable in the face of ADHD. "It's easy to get caught up in your surroundings and distractions but take deep breaths (try holding your breath for ten seconds at a time), close your eyes, and zero in on what you're feeling instead of what's going on around you."[73]

A lot of the advice I see online is centred around the idea of setting up a safe masturbation space for exploration, which is fair. But how does this even work when you're ADHD and your time keeping or self-care skills may not be as easily activated as a neurotypical's are? "I'll stop working in half an hour," I would say to R before realising I was still there two hours later, and she'd gone to bed without a cuddle or any sex. This happens in my solo sex life too. I go to bed intending to get off after some research, and then three hours have passed and it's two in the morning. Maybe I was just not trying hard enough. So I booked a night off to spend time with myself. I made sure I have batteries in the house, the right lighting, lube on standby, and some ethical porn too.

When the big night came around, I was exhausted and distracted. This is my default setting these days, so I let myself cancel the date on myself. I half-heartedly tried to reschedule but I just couldn't bring myself to do it. My time-keeping and booking time off has failed completely, because I can't force my mind to be in a particular mood when I want it to be. Therein lies the problem with time-keeping in reality for ADHD people. We cannot force it.

Self-Love and Emotional Distress

"If you can't love yourself, how in the hell are you

gonna love somebody else?" RuPaul

If I'm going to talk about self-love then I need to cover self-kindness too. I have generalised anxiety disorder which can be triggered by the RSD I experience as part of my ADHD. This in turn can cause panic attacks, which can seemingly come out of nowhere.

One of my more recent panic attacks left me standing in the middle of a field in a rural area alone. I was in tears as it was two weeks before Christmas and a few days before my annual leave kicked in. I was exhausted from deadlines, pandemics, lockdowns, and a lack of human contact for months. A silly mistake at work thanks to my inattentive ADHD had kick-started my anxiety to the stage where I suddenly started to wonder if this feeling was going to be it for the rest of my life.

I couldn't stand feeling so useless and awful. With tears streaming down my face, I contemplated killing myself. How much more of this could I take? I had to accept that ADHD was weighing me down and making me an extra burden on friends and family. I would never have a relationship or hold down a job properly. I also hadn't slept in three weeks, because my hyperactivity was unbearable. Lockdown had wiped out the coping mechanisms that I had spent years perfecting so I could deal with the everyday.

I had no idea what to do but I knew it was serious. Hope had left me alone in a desert where I'd become brittle and broken.

In their fantastic book on ADHD, Sari Solden and Michelle Frank discuss the danger of absorbed messages. "The experience of living with ADHD can feel like a lifetime of small assaults, resulting in the emotional distress syndrome…a chronic state of emotional stress, stress directly related to the struggle to live life with ADHD, a stress that breaks down emotional tolerance, stamina, and the ability to maintain a strong sense of well-being and spiritual health. Mistaken beliefs about ourselves might also have taken root through a more insidious route: by absorbing cultural and media messages or observing the behaviours of neurotypical girls and women to whom we compare ourselves. This may have happened without our conscious awareness, but these constant messages have coloured our ideas about what is expected of women, what is valued in women, and what is definitely not valued (like ADHD symptoms)."[74]

I've never put my hand up and asked for extra help because of my ADHD. I grew up in a country that demanded silence about any weaknesses someone might have. That left me crying in a field and unable to pick up the phone to ask for help when I clearly needed it.

Some ADHD experts claim that by the time ADHD children are ten, they've received 20,000 more negative messages from parents, peers, and others. Certainly in my case, I grew up thinking I was a burden on people and doomed to failure later in life. Those messages infiltrated my soul, and they're damned hard to get rid of.

I don't describe my parents as overly critical of me, but the overprotective thing is true. This isn't without just cause though, as we don't process risk like neurotypical people do so there was a lot at stake.

I removed myself from the Catholic church at

fourteen and stopped being taught by nuns at the age of eighteen. A lot of their negative voices faded away, but some comments have stayed with me. I don't think that cruelty will ever properly let my soul heal. Where there was silence that was normally filled with criticism, I picked up the slack and became my own worst enemy. I beat myself up every time my ADHD let me down. I looked at my neurotypical friends who were absolutely winning at life and wondered, why am I such a mess?

Once I got home from the episode in the field, I picked up the phone and made a few calls. I called my GP first and asked her to refer me to an ADHD specialist so I could get adult support. I also begged for sleeping tablets. I called a counselling service and rebooked a course of CBT to help me manage the anxiety. Then I called emergency talking services and howled down the phone to them for half an hour until I felt I was in a safer space. There were no two ways about it, I had to get safe and get serious about my health.

In her book, *Mad Girl*, Bryony Gordon talks about how difficult CBT can be when you're neurodiverse. "CBT is hard because it's basically making your brain do the complete opposite of what it has done forever. It's asking you to go cold turkey from all the ludicrous rituals and compulsions you have done for years and years and years. In my case, as someone with OCD, it is not about getting rid of the intrusive thoughts I have because you will never do that. What CBT does is change the way you respond to the thoughts. Because they are just thoughts. They don't necessarily mean anything."[75]

While Bryony used her CBT to break up the thoughts that something bad might happen if they didn't take part in rituals, I used it to break up my negative cycle of self-abuse. It's not easy given that anxiety and worry, along with all that glorious negativity, gives me a stimulating buzz which my brain craves. So it's very hard to break the habit of a lifetime, but even more so when your brain doesn't want to give it up. As we feel anxious, we produce cortisol, the stress hormone which causes the fight or flight feeling when we panic. High levels of cortisol can be addictive, causing you to enjoy, in a weird way, the feeling of being anxious. Cortisol can affect dopamine, but there are plenty of conflicting studies for you to rabbit-hole with. Some say it can deplete the levels of dopamine in the brain, while others say it can give you a release of it.

I have often suspected that a small, tiny part of my brain buzzes on anxiety and negative thought. Although this makes it a lot harder to give up in the long run. Also, if you hear all this negativity for long enough then you start to believe it. You start to believe you don't deserve kindness, love, or decent jobs. I suspect others who enjoy hunting humans for emotional sport (otherwise known as bullies) can sense this, which is why I had an issue with a former boss who loved to prey on these insecurities despite knowing I wasn't mentally healthy at the time.

In the meantime, I'm trying to practice self-kindness. I unpack the statements in my head. I'm not going to get fired today but even if I did, I would survive. It's about seeing the logic behind the panic. I also practice being kind when I'm at my most negative in front of the mirror too. It seems like a madness or a radical act to care enough about myself that I practice self-kindness.

This can be a good practice with our ADHD traits

too. It's easy to see the negatives. But if we flip the script, it can also make me a ton more productive and employable. We're seldom taught to see our ADHD as a superpower, but it can be. We're a lot of fun to be around because of our need to be stimulated and our excessive levels of energy. We can be spontaneous due to our lack of calculating risks, but spontaneity can be sexy in a relationship too. We don't feel the fear, but we definitely do it anyway. And that can lead to some really awesome things.

It can take a while to get it right, but if I can do it after a lifetime of nuns, Catholic guilt, rural schooling, and the Irish sense of humour, then anyone can.

Chapter Eight
And Then, There It Was

I don't know how it crept up on me, but one day I
felt different.

It was a completely random Saturday morning
mid-September when I took a seat on my grey
couch with a cup of steaming hot coffee in my hand.
The couch was new, so this was the only time in its
life where it wouldn't be covered in cat claw marks
or various spillages. I curled my feet up under me
and burrowed into the velvety cushions that I had
scattered across the seats, breathing in the fumes of
the terrible instant coffee I was holding.

The beaten-up, old record player whirred into
action, and the needle dropped on the album I
had selected to play. I tried to place the emotion
I felt. It was a new and slightly foreign feeling of
contentment.

My purchase of the house had been a complete
surprise to all but a select few I had chosen to
confide in. I'd started to put secret lump sums into
a shiny new bank account when I returned from
Italy. It was as if my gallivanting around Europe had
gotten all my mad energy out, and now I was ready
to make an actual life for myself. No one wants
to be the oldest swinger in the club, I told myself
when I cancelled nights out to save money instead.
Meanwhile, I started replacing my Tinder apps with
real estate sites as I swiped right to see hot, local
properties in my area on the way to work.

I don't know at what point I realised I wasn't returning to Ireland any time soon, but I suspect that it was confirmed when I signed on the digital dotted line and bought an actual real-life home. When had things gotten this serious? I panicked that this meant the end of my professional irresponsibility.

The first year of home ownership happened at the same time as the breakup from R. It wasn't until the following January that I realised an entire year had passed, and this was now the year I had planned on proposing to R. That had been the plan before it became apparent that I was ready to move in, propose to, and live life as a we but she wasn't. She had wanted to hold on to the last few years of late nights, rented apartments, and carefree drinks. There were five years between us that suddenly felt like twenty. I was ready for a quiet life.

One day, it had started to feel like home instead of the black hole that I bled my wages into. Still, I kept fixing breaks and wailing down the phone to my mother, "Another repair. What am I going to do?" Then the repairs started to tail off, and I was left with the realisation that I was coping.

I stayed single during this time, because there was no way anyone could understand the pressure I was under. I coped alone and grew up so much faster because of it. My hyperfocus on fixing the house meant I got an entire home decorated, painted, and mostly finished in under three months. So, I genuinely hadn't noticed my lack of communication with R for a good six months before it finally hit me.

The pandemic had been a blessing in disguise in this respect. We didn't have to face each other in the clubs in Nottingham because none of them were allowed to open. It was a truly amicable breakup. There were no split friend groups or screaming matches over text messages. We just ceased to exist as a couple, and that was that. The house distracted me from the worst of it as my hyperfocus took over my usual obsessive breakup behaviours. I would normally go over breakup problems repeatedly until I couldn't take it anymore. But things had changed. I'd somehow learned to let go…

So that morning, on that couch, on that Saturday, with that cat beside me, I felt an unfamiliar feeling that I couldn't place.

I paused and thought about it. It was pride mixed with contentment. I could be hungover, or I could be rushing to go to the vegan market down the road, but I wasn't. I was content to just switch off and feel at peace with the world. Let everyone else carry on without me, I'd thought. I was having a rare moment where my ADHD was silenced by how nice it felt to exist without the pressure of hyperactivity. These moments do exist, but they're rare for me. I don't know how or when they'll occur, but they're to be savoured, because I don't know when I'll get another. Enjoying silence is a big deal for me.

The house purchase was the first big signifier that I was putting down roots and achieving those goals as an adult that we're all expected to. I had managed to do it a bit later than others but then, I had done it alone. The house and to some extent, the planned proposal to R, were a result of feeling a societal pressure to achieve milestones. No one ever placed these pressures on me verbally, but the expectations were there, nonetheless. I wanted to show my parents that they didn't have to worry anymore, because I would be the best adult, one who would go on to do all the grown-up things expected of me.

I had another, more pressing reason for getting this done sooner rather than later.

While I was living in Italy, my father broke the news to me that he had cancer. We were sitting at a sticky table in the corner of my local bar in the centre of the city with a bowl of crisps between us. Over the ensuing five years, we got acquainted with cancer terminology with relative ease. It was hard to imagine life before pills, scans, and surgeries. Each Christmas and every trip home that I made, I remained silently grateful that I had been given this time to create memories. We knew that time wouldn't always be on our side but for now, it was. With cancer now in the picture, the race to reach responsible adulthood intensified. I was aware of my status as someone working adjacent to my dream career but not in it, and that I wasn't in a solid relationship. I worried that my father may never meet the person I wanted to marry because I hadn't even met this person yet. I felt a flicker of guilt that I would never give them grandkids despite my utter rejection of parenthood. I embraced the scripts and pressures I had grown up with and rebelled against as a teenager.

My father (da) comes from a generation of Irish das who were the strong, silent type. He isn't one for emotion or compliments, so naturally I've spent my whole life looking for both from him.

Faced with the prospect of losing him, I realised there was another clock placed on my biological table.

To be clear, my parents never called me a burden

or referred to me as such. But I know full well that I was a difficult child and caused a lot more grief than I'm probably even aware of. I'm desperate now to make up for lost time.

I've put a lot of pressure on myself as a result. I don't think I'm alone in this kind of familial pressure, but I do think we don't recognise when we're asking too much of ourselves. I also think we judge ourselves by neurotypical, straight standards. Not to mention throwing in the good old-fashioned Catholic guilt in there too.

(Straight) Queer Relationships

I don't feel like my relationships are less valid for being queer, but I do subconsciously set my standards by straight relationships. It's like a script I can follow where I know what's happening. It dictates how we behave around others. When it comes to relationships, it looks like in this episode, I fall in love with a partner, get married, buy a house, and have a child. That's the aspiration, right? However, for all I wanted this to happen, Irish law said no… Until it didn't, and we were faced with the prospect of a national vote on gay marriage.

I know when #marref happened, a strange thing happened in that there were some gays who openly said no. To vote for YES EQUALITY was to accept the linear, straight ideals of marriage, babies, and white picket fences. We had existed as others for so long that when we were offered the chance to come out of the cold, we weren't sure we wanted to. I voted yes for marriage equality while asking myself some serious questions at the same time. I recognised this argument as a rejection of the things that those who had rejected us held dear. Did I want to opt into all this pressure to get married?

Ultimately, I realised one day that I did. I was always going to vote yes in the referendum, that was a fact, but marriage mattered to me. I wanted the commitment, the rings, the faff, and most importantly, I wanted to make a vow to the person I loved no matter what gender they were.

But that put pressure on me, which got worse with time. A ticking time bomb of wanting to settle down. I felt a sickening pressure that hadn't been there before. I'd always thought I would find someone when I did.

My lack of engaging with my ADHD interfered with my meeting, falling in love, staying in love, contributing to a healthy relationship, and progressing towards marriage. Not to mention my dating pool was a lot smaller. Nottingham is many things but London, it is not. There are fewer people in the dating pool, albeit we have much cheaper venues to go for a first date in. I'm trying hard to break down my mental expectation that things aren't going to be what I expected and my married by forty goal might not get met.

In the book, *Cognitive-Behavioural Therapy for Sexual Dysfunction*, Michael Metz talks about this exact thing. "An individual's assumptions and standards become problematic when they are rigid and inaccurate or involve unrealistic views of individuals and relationships, which lead the person to be upset when real-life does not happen as desired."[76]

There is no quick fix to this. It takes years of working at it to undo all the years of subconsciously accepting that sometimes life doesn't look the way you want it to. I repeat positive, affirming thoughts when the panic of not doing things right sets in. You're neurodiverse, so you need to think more about what you need to get off or do things differently. You're a queer non-binary person, and that's okay. You may not get married or have kids, but you're fine. Having a partner or children isn't everything you think it is, and if you're alone for your life, then so be it.

There are always cats.

But I'm not always ready to go gently into that good night alone. You can accept your ADHD status, your single-ness, and cat owning enthusiasm without having to compromise on the need to be touched or loved. How amazing is it to be at a point in my life where I'm not only aware of my ADHD triggers and needs but almost ready to start communicating what I need to others?

Embracing ADHD When Dating

It wasn't a conscious decision to go back on Tinder or to look for a long-term relationship, but suddenly, post-lockdown nerves be damned, there I was. However, while dating as a neurodiverse person was difficult, dating as a neurodiverse person post-global pandemic and lockdowns was horrendous.

I found people had changed. *I* had changed. The landscape and rules had somehow changed. People were less interested in forming relationships and somehow, the atmosphere on the apps felt more toxic than before. It didn't help that the pandemic stole two very valuable years as I left the safety of my middle thirties and headed into my late thirties, where I began to ask questions of myself like, well,

do I want children? Do I care about marriage? It was
terrifying to think that the years I had for mentally
sorting that out were now gone.

I was sitting on my first date since R when I
decided to flip the script. I don't generally tell
people I have ADHD upfront, because I'd never
realised it was an issue that played a huge part in
my relationships. I'd only recently started to think
of ADHD as a part of me, so it had never occurred
to me that I needed to be honest about it. But
things were changing. My awareness of how my
ADHD impacts my life was changing. If we were
going to make it long-term, then we'd need to
know what could possibly be a problem going in.
After all, we weren't talking about a preference for
pineapple on pizza. We have so much to offer, but
we need to learn that what we offer looks different
to neurotypicals. Coaching, emotional heavy-
lifting, and education are key here. My style of
relationship means I am a whirlwind to be around
and to partner with, but I had never admitted to
my ADHD struggles when I should have. Hindsight
is a blessing and a curse, but it meant that I was
prepared to get into another relationship where I
knew what I was doing. *My ADHD is part of who
I am as a human being.* I sipped my cider while I
waited for an opening to somehow mention this.

The conversation lulled naturally as we looked at
each other, shy with first-date nerves. We were in
the Canalhouse, as it was one of the first smoking
area bars in Nottingham to open post-lockdown,
and it added a certain level of nerves to an already
anxious situation. The smell of hand sanitiser wafted
in over the summer breeze.

"So, what do you do for a living?" she asked,

playing with the rim of her wine glass.

I'd told her before over text message, but she'd either forgotten or was keen to fill the silence. I decided it's the latter, so I went straight in. "I'm a journalist normally," I said. "But I'm writing a book about ADHD and sex right now." I think it might have been my imagination, but my voice raised when I say the word sex so people at the table socially distant from us turned to look.

"It's not just ADHD and sex, but relationships and how our disorder affects how we behave," I continued. I was now heading into the territory of the classic ADHD overshare, where I was in danger of spilling far too many beans on the book.

"How does that work?" she asked curiously.

"Well," I said and put down my pint glass. "I have trouble getting into the idea of sex, and my orgasms can be non-existent. I'm really looking to see if there is a way I can challenge this and have better sex. And to help other people who might be dealing with a lot of these types of ADHD issues too."

She looked a bit taken aback, and I readied myself to reach for my bank card to pay.

"So if we were to have sex," she said slowly, "I'd be in the book then?"

"Erm, not if you don't want to be, no," I stammered. I was a bit shocked she hadn't run away.

"Well, let's see how we go then," she said, as the topic hung in the air between us.

I had somehow managed to bring up the topic of sex before we'd even finished our first pint. I find, somehow, that talk about the details became easier after the next four ciders that followed. "Sometimes I don't feel like sex or masturbation for months." I shrugged. I wasn't excusing bad sex etiquette but rather telling someone that I won't be having sex if my ADHD is interfering with my desire. I was tired of this cycle of guilt and lack of desire.

After that date, I realised that while I cared that the other person knows about the book, I no longer cared that the other person knew I was an ADHD person. It's absolutely not down to them to have an opinion on it. If you can't face dating someone with it—don't. Because we don't need that. I added ADHD pride to my social media bios that week, proudly informing people. I was sick of hiding it, and doing so was actually detrimental in the long run, both to people I was getting to know and to my own mental health. Despite my worries that I had branded myself unlovable before people have a chance to get to know me, no one seemed bothered by my declaring my ADHD status upfront. In fact, people were more curious about it than anything else, and I made some great connections with other folks as a result.

I decided after feeling brave following the dates I'd been on, that I would flip the script even further. After matching with a person in Lincoln who was polyamory, I decided to try it, given I had nothing to lose anymore. N had such a positive outlook on polyamory and explained that we had different needs that are impossible for one person to meet. We have different friends who have different strengths, so why not lovers too?

With this in mind, I started a relationship with N before starting one with another person in Nottingham. To further add to this, while drunk in a hot tub in the middle of a forest in the middle of nowhere, I reopened things with another ex-partner.

I kept dating as if collecting people for an imaginary scoreboard and went on lots of different dates, which didn't always end well. I kept up the pretence that everything was fine, and I was having a lot of fun when in reality, it really wasn't for me. I think successful polyamory can be done well, but when it isn't meant for you, it can leave you overwhelmed.

So I continued dating, with good and bad experiences.

I had a date go so bad that I had to get an Uber from Sheffield to Nottingham in a self-induced panic. Note to self: no matter how cute she is, don't ever let a trainee ADHD therapist offer directions to the train station after four large wines. I kept searching for that connection with someone that never came and each time, I became slightly more dejected and sad.

Embracing ADHD When It Comes to Sex

Dates aside, one area that improved was my sex life. I began tearing up the script entirely and asking for better sex. This, in the short term, had a big effect on the type of relationships I experienced when I got serious enough to sleep with them. I began to recognise my own needs and ask for them to be met.

In her book, *Don't Hold My Head Down*, Lucy-Anne Holmes investigates how to have better sex and tells how she came to recognise her own needs. I was blown away by the lengths she went to explore this by visiting sexologists and sex festivals.

"I considered myself. I was hardly making sex glorious in my own life. There I was at thirty-five, and I hadn't even skimmed the surface of how amazing sex could be. That was rather a sad realisation to have. I'd been sexually active for over twenty years, but I hadn't been that proactive. I wasn't thinking about what I wanted and how I wanted it. I hate to say it, but sex was something that just sort of happened to me. I was willing, more than willing, keen even—but I was always an actor in, rather than a director or writer, of the show."[77]

The pandemic gave me a lot of hurdles when it came to sex research, but I wasn't sure going to sexy festivals or therapists was for me. However, the acceptance and understanding of her own body that she gains by finally listening to it is something to take away from the book. I wanted to start being complicit in my own good sex instead of, somehow, accidentally in attendance. I needed desperately to understand my own ADHD in relation to relationships so that I could move on.

ADHD life coach Anastasia Galadza stressed that knowing what your traits look like and how to handle them means that as you age, you can take ownership of them. "You'll often hear the phrase, everyone's a little ADHD but that's in the same way everyone gets a bit depressed sometimes. It's the frequency, duration, and level of the impairment caused by those particular traits that make ADHD either your superpower or kryptonite. Get to know what your traits are over time, as you age, and accept they will look different. Knowing what those are makes a huge difference in not just accepting it but being able to name it. I think being able to name things gives you the power over it."

I wanted to have power over it. I was fed up with feeling like my body was broken, so I decided to ease the pressure of the life I felt I should have. I would need to start being active in the better sex I wanted if I was going to have anything at all. As Galadza said, things were changing with age. I was learning to name and accept the neurodivergent parts of me.

It wasn't going to be easy though. The culture of silence that I grew up in was all-consuming and hard to break. We're not taught to put our hands up and ask for better sex. There are several baseline things we need:

We need to learn to ask for better.

We need to practise more self-kindness.

We need to ask for more consideration.

We need to ask for better sex and more orgasms.

The right person will listen and together, you can work around the issues that arise. Alternatively, you can do what I did, write a book about your needs, tell a date about it, have a pint or six, then email the entire thing to them after weeks of dating before then having a panic attack. While I wouldn't suggest spending a year working on a novel will work for everyone, trust me that making lists and talking to your partner will.

Embracing ADHD in Relationships: Here We Go Again

I was standing in the middle of IKEA on a Thursday night holding a godtagbar when I realised how screwed I was. The person I was dating sneezed four times in a row, and I said, "Aw," thinking it was the cutest thing ever. I recognised it instantly; I was in trouble.

I don't know at what point it happened, but I'd managed to fall in love. After two years of utterly disastrous attempts to date post-breakup and lockdown, I had finally managed to fall back into being a we. I had gone back on Tinder with the promise that if it didn't work this time, I was fecking giving up, and swiped right. The result had been months of dinner and drink dates that had somehow meant that months on, this person, V, was still here.

This time I felt confident that I wasn't going to make the same mistakes, because I was so certain I had all the information now. I could self-analyse my way out of everything thanks to my endless hours of research, right?

Wrong.

In a haze of weekends away, meaningful cuddles, lingering kisses, sex, and fun dates, I had been in a hurry to announce my sexual brokenness was cured, but this meant I had glossed over the rest of the problems that were in the background. I sailed past my RSD thinking I was fixed, because the sex was good. As I mentioned earlier, RSD causes a significant problem for me in relationships and my work. I often see threats or problems that just aren't there. I look for signs, patterns, and triggers that give me a signal that someone is getting ready to leave me so that I can get in there first and go. I began looking for signs every single date that this wasn't working and I should walk away, which was absolutely exhausting.

ADHD people with RSD love to ruminate on things, so I would run the scenarios between V and myself over and over again in my brain trying to make sense of things. Suddenly, something that made sense at noon would be a cause for running away by three p.m.

In a desperate bid to find any help I could on

RSD cures before I broke my new relationship, I did the worst thing possible: I googled.

When interviewed for an article for the *Metro*, Anna Granta, a specialist life coach who trains neurodivergent people to rejoin the workforce, gave a few bits of practical advice on coping with RSD. She says you need to "acknowledge that it is real, that the pain is real, and that you are strong enough to experience that pain and keep going."[78]

In taking this on board, I try to stop myself when I can feel myself react to something I perceive as a threat. I take a second to acknowledge why this is happening and remind myself that I am loved, regardless of what I think. This can be harder some days more than others depending on if I am tired, hungover, stressed, or anxious.

Her second suggestion is to "go outside your comfort zone slightly and put yourself in situations that will stretch your tolerance for rejection just a little bit." To do this, I started taking classes for things I knew I was notoriously bad at, like ballet, just so I can feel myself fail. I reached out to new people in a bid to make new friends, and I started verbalising when I felt I needed reassurance. I also recognised that I needed to talk to V about all of these mini-experiments and talk more in general. Talking about trauma is a first for me in any relationship with anyone, and I've only recently been able to use the word. I have a lot of trauma around being left behind and not being good enough, and the ADHD which comes from my childhood and teenage years that I have simply swept under a giant rug and left there.

A third suggestion is that the link between a lack of serotonin and RSD could be helped by "spending time in the daylight each day, eating lots of different types of plants, and low-intensity exercise." All of this is stuff I'm already doing, but I recognise there is another thing that affects serotonin: alcohol.

"Alcoholics and experimental [lab] animals that consume large quantities of alcohol show evidence of differences in brain serotonin levels compared with non-alcoholic."[79] I wish I could tell you that I meticulously planned and used techniques to quit drinking, but the truth is that it was like a switch flipped. I just slowed to an almost-halt overnight after a heavy birthday celebration brought me to my knees in the morning. I realised, through a haze of self-hatred the next day, that I wasn't happy with this anymore. I stopped drinking for a month, then gradually introduced it again, dropping from several bottles of wine a week to the odd pint if I felt like it.

These experiments are ongoing in a relationship which is also ongoing, but I already feel better about it. As William Dodson notes, just having the words for RSD is enough to feel some power over the condition.

"Rejection sensitivity is part of ADHD. It's neurologic and genetic. Early childhood trauma makes anything worse, but it does not cause RSD. Often, patients are comforted just to know there is a name for this feeling. It makes a difference knowing what it is, that they are not alone, and that almost 100% of people with ADHD experience rejection sensitivity. After hearing this diagnosis, they're relieved to know it's not their fault and that they are not damaged."[80]

I point this out, because knowing about RSD is important so we can avoid the pain of making the same mistakes over again. However, I also realised how important it is to not see our work on ourselves as finished, because it never is. ADHD is such a complex, layered thing that I feel I will be deciphering myself for years yet. Also, a lot of us have very real trauma around our formative years as neurodiverse people, either diagnosed or undiagnosed. Those who are diagnosed later in life can feel a very real grief from thinking about the painful experiences that now make sense in light of the new information. Those of us who were diagnosed as children weren't given all the answers either, and as the first wave of the Ritalin Generation grow up, we are setting the standards of what ADHD adults look like.

I still believe in working on yourself, but communication and support from a partner is vital for a relationship's survival. In keeping things silent, I haven't always been the best version of myself that I could be. Thankfully, I have time to address this.

Support and Care

Female entrepreneur Raven Faber once told me while I was interviewing her for the magazine I wrote for, "I don't care how badass you think you are, you will need support." This was in relation to advice she would give to someone who was thinking of starting a small business, but I think it applies to damn near everything.

I think she was right in so many ways but in particular about how we find our community. We need a thing to belong to. As humans, we are mad for belonging and feeling accepted. I cherish my queer and Irish communities. These same people can offer me condolences when I post about a breakup, and a bunch of gay folk offer virtual hugs and counselling. So this entrepreneur was right, you need support from your people. It isn't weakness, and you can still be a badass.

There has been a huge shift towards embracing those who are waiting on or choosing not to get a diagnosis. Only you can decide if diagnosis is right for you or not, but learning more about how you function as a person is never a bad thing. You can get a lot of support from people who aren't doctors but be careful how much advice you take from Facebook doctors in the comment section.

The conversations I've had with other people about their ADHD is balanced by the help I'm able to get professionally from doctors. I won't take advice on how much of whatever medication is best for me from social media, but I will rant about losing my house keys—again.

It isn't up to social media to do the heavy lifting when it comes to mental health or balancing neurodiversity. There's a gap between the professional services and the online peer support that can leave people dangerously without help. This is where support services need to get better and step up but also where we need to learn to ask for help. Help can be hindered though if those designing it see ADHD as an "altered ability" rather than a disability. It can be difficult to access services if you live far from them.

Help can also be expensive. If you're low income or are disabled, then this is a nightmare. We need to ask how we can start reducing the cost of healthcare in Ireland or accessibility in England, because our government certainly seem unconcerned with the cost of accessing essential care. I'm blessed to be able to access the NHS in Nottingham, and I don't take a minute of it for granted. My referrals have been free and so has a lot of my CBT work. It has saved my life at a time when I needed help the most.

When I stood in the middle of the park with tears streaming down my face because I felt my ADHD was going to ruin my life, I also felt alone and scared. It doesn't have to feel this way at all. We do have to get better about asking for help and getting support though. This is even more so if we fall into a minority within a minority as a queer, trans, non-binary, or person of colour. Your voice and place within neurodiversity becomes even more important, and it is a form of activism. For example, I learned that I don't have to accept help designed for straight folks as a queer person. I can ask that it be tailored to me or for the person acknowledge my queerness by using the correct pronouns.

Try it. You count, and you are worth it.

I refer once again to Laura James' excellent book on autism, *Odd Girl Out.* "I am not what I expect either and still, a year on from my diagnosis, I am fighting to live a neurotypical life. Where did that get me? Nowhere I wanted to be. I was sad, burnt-out, lonely, demoralised, and confused."[81]

She continues: "The importance of environment begins to make sense on an emotional level. I need to stop trying to be less autistic and start creating an environment in which I can thrive in my autism. I must leave the shadows of an imperfect past and start living in the now."

"One of the things people don't realise about ADHD is that they recognise patterns where no one [else] sees them," Anastasia told me over Zoom at one of our meetings. "Not even patterns but how things relate to each other as you connect the dots in your head to things that are interesting to you. The ADHD brain can go into a room and see things that look seemingly unrelated, but that's what artists are like. A lot of people with ADHD are artists, because they see things that are abstract and put them together."

When I'm asked to do something complex at work or a friend asks me for my input on something, I'm working on these abstract connections in my head. I've started to challenge myself a little to speak up if I'm feeling stressed out. If I'm going to change myself and do all of this research, then I will also be expecting those around me to do a bit of work too.

So when things are a bit overwhelming, I ask myself why.

When I forget to do a task because I haven't written it down, I ask myself why.

By asking why these things have happened, I can take ownership for them, and I'm learning to shut out that little voice that tells me I need to feel guilty about it.

When I asked ADHD people for an interview for this book, they got excited and nearly all of them asked for a deadline for their submission. A lot of people do this, and you can argue it's unique to ADHD folk, but we all acknowledge that responses like, "Oh, whenever," or "No rush" don't work for us. We need a concrete date, time, and procedure to follow so that things get done. If you find that someone is being super casual about something they've asked you to do and it's making you anxious, speak up. Explain that you need something concrete in order to be confident you can get it done. It's that proactive thing; don't let life just happen. Take it by its leash and lead it where you want it to go.

Separating ADHD and Self

In the book, *Radical Acceptance of ADHD* by Sari Solden and Michelle Frank, they ask us to stop fighting our natural behaviours and lean into it.

"Fighting against a part of your experience is like trying to punch your way out of quicksand. The more your fight, the more doomed you are to sinking. Dropping the struggle against what distresses you, and therefore moving into acceptance, produces more effective, lasting results than trying to get rid of the distress. The more we avoid that which brings discomfort, the more likely we are to keep having that discomfort."[82]

They continue: "Radical acceptance is the willingness to experience ourselves and life as it is."

In radically accepting my ADHD and reaching out to women, non-binary, and transgender folk, I started to notice something happening that I coined "hyper acceptance." I have no idea if this is a term or not, so I'm going to pretend for a second that it is.

I started to see a lot of posts where people discussed their symptoms at length. I noticed traits I had and some I didn't. There was a quick eagerness of some of the people posting to put a lot of their issues onto ADHD when it sounded like potentially they weren't. ADHD seemed to get a lot of blame for random things from lost keys to vitamin D deficiency.

It can be very easy to self-diagnose your traits or accept some that don't quite fit if you're just using online sources, especially when you're first diagnosed or realise you may have it; it's tempting to make everything fit. However, if you don't see yourself in the big books or understand the language, then these sources may be all you have.

I ask Shar if they'd noticed any of this faulty blame of ADHD online. They nodded thoughtfully before agreeing that there was a tendency to feel pressure from social media which had been egged on by lockdown boredom.

"I think there is an aspect of almost cabin fever coming in some of these spaces as well. All we have to do right now is scroll on social media, and that can be our whole world. We nearly need to be like, am I holding myself up to my own standards? Or am I holding myself up to the magic social media standards, where everyone is showing their best fish or making their most articulate points." They think about it before adding, "It's probably lockdown influence."

One day, in a conversation with my friend D, who also has ADHD, they mentioned they find their internalised hyperactivity results in twitches. I don't experience this as twitches but as itching. After a lengthy time of sitting still, my body will create itches for me to move and scratch. However, I don't have twitches like D, which is a great example of how we can have the same brain type but present totally differently to each other.

Where does my ADHD begin and my personality end? I don't want to let myself become my diagnosis to the point where it clouds over everything. I'm me. That includes my ADHD, right? It corresponded with posts I saw in the ADHD partner groups too, that neurotypical folks were confused about what simply constituted bad behaviour and how much of it was beyond that person's control. In some more extreme cases, there was physical violence, which should never be tolerated, but the milder posts asked for help. They wanted to support their loving partners but needed to get mad on occasion and didn't want to scold someone for something they couldn't control. It's important to recognise that we all have needs and our emotions, neurodiverse or neurotypical, are valid. These can be murky bog waters, but communication will keep all of us from drowning.

I began my ADHD life by not wanting to talk about it, but now I don't want to shut up talking about it or assessing myself.

My point here is that research, connection, and chat is fantastic. Anastasia was right that knowing what's wrong with you or different about you gives you a power over it. However, it's important not to get lost in a diagnosis and let it take over your life. You have to accept that your personality is a lot of who you are too. My ADHD may make me forget to cancel my subscriptions, but my personality means I'm a very open-minded person who takes out subscriptions, because I'm endlessly curious. I'm possibly open-minded because I'm LGBT+ too, but I'm going to go with personality. It's so tempting to overlook our more negative traits and blame them on ADHD, but that helps no one. I fully accept that I am overly extroverted in a loud way that can grate on people, and I'm terribly impatient. These aren't parts of my ADHD, but my ADHD can interact with them, making them more exaggerated.

I did, at one stage, become too focused on examining my relationships through the lens of ADHD. I forgot the crucial fact that sometimes relationships just don't work out. Personalities clash. We're not simpatico. Sometimes sex is just bad, and we don't want to have it. Not everything needs to be a big meaningful thing or attributed to ADHD.

My mother asked me recently if I thought my relationship with R would have survived if the pandemic hadn't happened and my ADHD was better controlled. I mean, these aren't small things, and it's very telling that my breakup happened right as the entire world was under a massive amount of stress. Is it possible we'd given up during a tough patch where we should have worked it out? If I had gone on medication for my ADHD and researched it a bit more, then would we potentially work through it together?

No. I don't think so, and I'm glad it hasn't.

One thing that Anastasia helped me to realise almost a year later was how R and I worked so well to be able to date for so long, even though we ended up not working. In many ways, we were both into the same things, like travel, good wine, and politics, but in others we were opposites. She was quiet and introverted to my loud, brash exterior. She provided a nice, calming alternative to be around, whereas I could be a bit of car crash at times. Anastasia said, "If you have an introverted, neurotypical person, then they can get attached to the idea that the person may get them out of their shell. People are attracted to ADHD people because it can be so fun. It can be super healthy and make for a really fulfilling relationship."

If she was attracted to me for my wild streak, then

I liked that she was a steady and secure person. I felt she took care of me when I was emotionally flared up. I cheered her on. This can be a good balance or at its worst, it can be unhealthy. Being able to recognise that now makes me feel better about things. Sure, my ADHD was an element of our relationship, because it's part of me. But it was also a personality and timing thing. It was…life.

The most important lesson I took away from R was not to give up so easily, and if someone is worth it, to put in the effort. I was so focused on my career, my social life, and everything else around me that I failed to stop and put effort into the relationship I had in front of me.

I had to learn to slow down and take time to nurture my actual relationships with people. I'm aware of how cheesy and self-help book that sounds, but it's true. I also learned that I need to be aware of what ADHD looks like for me in relationships and to communicate that. R had no idea what was happening, so it allowed the anxiety she felt to take over, and she internalised way worse than it actually was. Someday, I will apologise for that properly.

There were lessons to be learned from S too. These were some sad realisations. On the way home from a day in Skegness, where all the best lessons are learned, I realised that the party was over. I spent my twenties with a man who had no intention of ever leaving the party before the lights came on. He was determined to be the last man standing despite the marriages, babies, and engagements around him.

I deserved and wanted more than that for myself. I learned to put my own wants and needs first, starting with a glorious relocation to Italy for a year. I learned I didn't want to accept less than what I deserved, and I shouldn't have to.

In accepting the lessons from both relationships, I've been able to set my brain free. The freedom has allowed me to move on. I wasn't ready to meet someone or even entertain a relationship until I had dealt with the demons attached to S, R, and ADHD. Now, with V, I'm putting all this research, all this learning, all this often-painful growth into our relationship. Hopefully, it will help smooth the rough patches as we navigate life together. That's what being human is, right? With ADHD or without it, we're all navigating the world as best we can.

That afternoon on that couch in my living room, I realised I was content. I had a lovely home that I had made my own, and I got to write every day for a living like I had wanted to as a child. All the assessments, research, and soul-searching for this book has left me in a good place. Most importantly, it taught me about myself. It taught me about who I am and how I function in the world. It taught me that there's hope, and I am worthy of love.

And how fucking amazing is that?

References

Chapter Two: Sex, Love, and...Adult ADHD

1 - Main, B. (2022) *ADHD & Obsessive Thoughts: How to Stop the Endless Analysis. ADDitude* magazine. (https://www.additudemag.com/adhd-and-obsessive-thoughts-too-clingy-insecure/)

2 - Perez, C.C. (2019) *Invisible Women: Exposing data bias in a world designed for men.* New York: Penguin Random House. Chapter: Yentl Syndrome. pp.22-23

Chapter Three: What Is ADHD Anyway?

3 - The Centers for Disease Control and Prevention (CDC) (2022) *Parent survey and ADHD facts.* (https://www.cdc.gov/ncbddd/adhd/data.html)

4 - Finnegan, B. (2022) *Four Times as Many Boys Being Diagnosed with ADHD than Girls.* Today FM News. (https://www.todayfm.com/news/four-times-as-many-boys-getting-diagnosed-with-adhd-than-girls-1388568)

5 - NHS England (2021) *Health A-Z: Attention Deficit Disorder (ADHD) "Symptoms"* (https://www.nhs.uk/conditions/attention-deficit-hyperactivity-disorder-adhd/symptoms/)

6 - *ACAS Equality Act 2010: What Disability Means by Law: The Disability and Equality Act.* (https://

www.acas.org.uk/what-disability-means-by-law)

7 - Butler, M. (2021) Tweet uploaded on January 14, 2021 (https://twitter.com/MaryButlerTD/status/1349684599878778881)

8 - O'Halloran, M. and Power, J. (2021) *Josepha Madigan Apologises for 'Normal Children Comment.* Irish Times Online. (https://www.irishtimes.com/news/politics/josepha-madigan-apologises-for-normal-children-comment-1.4458779)

9 - NHS Inform Scotland (2021) *Attention Deficit Hyperactive Disorder. Section on Diagnosis.* (https://www.nhsinform.scot/illnesses-and-conditions/mental-health/attention-deficit-hyperactivity-disorder-adhd#diagnosis)

10 - The NHS Foundation (2022) *The Neurodiversity Charity. About us section. One in five statistic.* (https://www.adhdfoundation.org.uk/about-us/)

11 - Chung W, Jiang S, Paksarian D, et al. (2019) *Trends in the Prevalence and Incidence of Attention-Deficit/Hyperactivity Disorder Among Adults and Children of Different Racial and Ethnic Groups.* JAMA Network Open. (https://jamanetwork.com/journals/jamanetworkopen/fullarticle/2753787)

12 - Danielson, M.L. et al (2018) *Prevalence of Parent-Reported ADHD Diagnosis and Associated Treatment Among U.S. Children and Adolescents. Journal of Clinical Child & Adolescent Psychology.* 47:2, pp.199-212, (https://www.ncbi.nlm.nih.gov/pmc/articles/PMC5834391/pdf/nihms937906.pdf) and *ADDitude* magazine. (https://www.

additudemag.com/statistics-of-adhd)

13 - Eliscu, J. (2000) *Q&A: Wes Borland of Limp Bizkit. Rolling Stone* Magazine.

14 - Higuera, V. (2022) *"What is Rejection Sensitivity Dysphoria?"* Healthline. p.26

15 - Dodson, W. (2022) *How ADHD Ignites Rejection Sensitive Dysphoria. ADDitude* magazine. (https://www.additudemag.com/rejection-sensitive-dysphoria-and-adhd/)

Chapter Four: The Art of Distraction

16 - Herbenic, D. et al (2017) *Women's Experiences with Genital Touching, Sexual Pleasure, and Orgasm: Results from a U.S. Probability Sample of Women Ages 18 to 94* (https://www.tandfonline.com/doi/abs/10.1080/0092623X.2017.1346530)

17 - Bijlenga, D. et al (2017) *Prevalence of Sexual Dysfunctions and Other Sexual Disorders in Adults with Attention-Deficit/Hyperactivity Disorder Compared to the General Population.* (https://link.springer.com/article/10.1007/s12402-017-0237-6)

18 - Aron, N.R. (2020) *Good Morning, Destroyer of Men's Souls: A Memoir of Women, Addiction, and Love.* New York: Penguin. p.18

19 - Hepola, S (2015) *Blackout, Remembering the Things I Drank to Forget.* London: Two Roads. p.6

20 - Zulauf, C.A., Sprich, S.E., Safren, S.A., & Wilens, T.E. (2014) *The Complicated Relationship between Attention Deficit/Hyperactivity Disorder* *and Substance Use Disorders.* Current psychiatry reports. 16(3), p.436. (https://www.additudemag.com/statistics-of-adhd/)

21 - Lee, S.S. et al. (2011) *Prospective Association of Childhood Attention-Deficit/Hyperactivity Disorder (ADHD) and Substance Use and Abuse/ Dependence: A Meta-Analytic Review. Clinical Psychology Review.* Vol. 31,3: p/328-41. (https://www.sciencedirect.com/science/article/pii/S0272735811000110?via%3Dihub.) (https://www.additudemag.com/statistics-of-adhd/)

22 - Aron, N.R. (2020) *Good Morning, Destroyer of Men's Souls: A Memoir of Women, Addiction, and Love.* New York: Penguin. pp.185-186

23 - Orlov, M. and Kohlenberger, N. (2014) *The Couple's Guide to Thriving with ADHD.* North Branch: Speciality Press US. p.5

24 - South, F. (2022) *Opening up about ADHD and alcoholism. ADDitude* magazine. (https://www.additudemag.com/opening-up-about-adhd-and-alcoholism/)

25 - Gordon, B. (2016) *Mad Girl: A Happy Life with a Mixed-up Mind.* London: Headline Publishing Group. pp.161-163

26 - Hepola, S. (2015) *How to Date Online When You Are Stone Cold Sober. Elle* Magazine. (https://www.elle.com/life-love/sex-relationships/a28169/online-dating-sober/)

27/28 - Solden, S. and Frank, M. (2019) *A Radical Guide for Women with ADHD: Embrace*

Neurodiversity and Live Boldly and Break Through Barriers. Oakland: New Harbinger Publications. p.112

29 - Hergenrather, J.Y. et al (2020) *Cannabinoid and Terpenoid Doses are Associated with Adult ADHD Status of Medical Cannabis Patients.* Rambam Maimonides Medical Journal. Volume 11, Issue 1. (https://www.rmmj.org.il/userimages/1036/1/PublishFiles/1038Article.pdf)

Chapter Five: Hyperfocus, Dopamine Rushes, and Obsessive Crushes... Oh My!

30 - Solden, S. and Frank, M. (2019) *A Radical Guide for Women with ADHD: Embrace Neurodiversity and Live Boldly and Break Through Barriers.* Oakland: New Harbinger Publications. p.X

31 - Anon. (2022) *Epidemiology: do symptoms of ADHD differ between genders?* ADHD Institute. Last accessed 24.11.22 (https://adhd-institute.com/burden-of-adhd/epidemiology/)

32 - Solden, S. and Frank, M. (2019) *A Radical Guide for Women with ADHD: Embrace Neurodiversity and Live Boldly and Break Through Barriers.* Oakland: New Harbinger Publications. p.X

33 - Orlov, M. and Kohlenberger, N. (2014) *The Couple's Guide to Thriving with ADHD.* North Branch: Speciality Press US. p.5

34 - Orlov, M. and Kohlenberger, N. (2014) *The Couple's Guide to Thriving with ADHD.* North Branch: Speciality Press US. p.55

35 - Legg, T.J. et al (2018) *What effect does ADHD have on sexuality?* Medical News Today. (https://www.medicalnewstoday.com/articles/321860.)

36 - Dodson, W. (2022) *Three defining features of ADHD that everyone overlooks.* ADDitude magazine. (https://www.additudemag.com/symptoms-of-add-hyperarousal-rejection-sensitivity/)

37 - Taylor, M. (2019) *Is There a Link between ADHD and Dopamine?* Greatist. (https://greatist.com/adhd/adhd-dopamine)

38 – O'Dougherty, D. (1999) *Dopamine Transporter Density in Patients with Attention Deficit Hyperactivity Disorder.* The Lancet. (https://www.thelancet.com/journals/lancet/article/PIIS0140-6736(99)04030-1/fulltext)

39 - Legg, T.J. et al (2019) *Is there a link between ADHD and dopamine?* Medical News Today. (https://www.medicalnewstoday.com/articles/325499)

40 - Spiegel, Tali et al (2019) *Attention Deficit/Hyperactivity Disorder and Increased Engagement in Sexual Risk-Taking Behavior: The Role of Benefit Perception.* Frontiers in Psychology. (https://www.ncbi.nlm.nih.gov/pmc/articles/PMC6538875/)

41 - Orlov, M. and Kohlenberger, N. (2014) *The Couple's Guide to Thriving with ADHD.* North Branch: Speciality Press US. p.47

Chapter Six: How Kinky Sex Can Help Us

42 - Crenshaw, W. (2022) *The Birds, the Bees & ADHD: Teaching Your Teen About Sex—Mindfully.* *ADDitude* magazine. https://www.additudemag.com/talking-about-sex-with-your-teen-with-adhd/

43 - James, L. (2018) *Odd Girl Out: An Autistic Woman in a Neurotypical World.* Colorado: Bluebird. p.96

44 - Asitflies, J. (2018) *Chronic Sex: How BDSM Helps Me Manage My ADHD.* Available from: (https://www.chronicsex.org/2018/09/bdsm-adhd/)

45 - Lajole, Y. (2020) *Kink Helped My Mental Health: The Healing Benefits of BDSM.* Refinery 29. Updated version 2.2.20. (https://www.refinery29.com/en-gb/2020/12/10201340/kink-bdsm-positive-impact-mental-health)

46 - Orlov, M. and Kohlenberger, N. (2014) *The Couple's Guide to Thriving with ADHD.* North Branch: Speciality Press US. p.47

47 - Wallace, M. (2020) *The Queer Faces of ADHD: Nora Nord's Photography Project Highlights the Under-Represented Beauty in Neurodiversity.*

48 - Asitflies, J. (2018) *Chronic Sex: How BDSM Helps Me Manage My ADHD.* (https://www.chronicsex.org/2018/09/bdsm-adhd/)

49 - James, L. (2018) *Odd Girl Out: An Autistic Woman in a Neurotypical World.* Colorado: Bluebird. p.189

50/51 - Anon. (2020) *ADHD Partner Dominant in BDSM Relationship.* ADHD forum on Reddit.

52 - Strang, J. (2018) *Why We Need to Respect Sexual Orientation, Gender Diversity in Autism Spectrum.*

53 - Solden, S. and Frank, M. (2019) *A Radical Guide for Women with ADHD: Embrace Neurodiversity and Live Boldly and Break Through Barriers.* Oakland. New Harbinger Publications. Chapter 4. p.58

54/55 - Solden, S. and Frank, M. (2019) *A Radical Guide for Women with ADHD: Embrace Neurodiversity and Live Boldly and Break Through Barriers.* Oakland. New Harbinger Publications. Chapter 3. p.31

56 - Downs, A. (2005) *The Velvet Rage: Overcoming the Pain of Growing Up Gay in a Straight Man's World.* Chapter one: The little boy with the big secret. Boston: Da Capo Press. p.15

57 - Novotini, M. (2020) *It Always Takes More Than Just Two Minutes.* (https://www.additudemag.com/adult-time-management-tips/)

58 - Anon. (2015) *Subs With ADHD, How Do You Do It?* Reddit forum.

59 - Anon. (2015) *Subs With ADHD, How Do You Do It?* Reddit forum.

Chapter Seven: Me, Myself, and I: Solo Sex and the Art of Kindness

60 - Shepard, E. (2019) *Kinked and Crippled: Disabled BDSM Practitioners: Experiences and Embodiments of Pain. A personal story.* PhD thesis. Edge Hill University. p.24 Available at https://research.edgehill.ac.uk/en/studentTheses/kinked-and-crippled-disabled-bdsm-practitioners-experiences-and-e

61 - Comella, L. (2017) *Vibrator Nation: How Feminist Sex-Toy Stores Changed the Business of Pleasure.* Durham. Duke University Press. p.68

62 - Comella, L. (2017) *Vibrator Nation: How Feminist Sex-Toy Stores Changed the Business of Pleasure.* Durham: Duke University Press. p.223

63 - Comella, L. (2017) *Vibrator Nation: How Feminist Sex-Toy Stores Changed the Business of Pleasure.* Durham. Duke University Press. p.175

64/65 - Comella, L. (2017) *Vibrator Nation: How Feminist Sex-Toy Stores Changed the Business of Pleasure.* Durham. Duke University Press. p.180

66 - Weiss, S. and Ekemezie, C. (2021) *10 Little-Known Ways Women Masturbate.* bustle.com (https://www.bustle.com/wellness/ways-women-masturbate-that-you-might-not-know-about)

67 - Harvey, L. (2020) *Masturbation: The Love That Dare Not Speak Its Name. Glamour* magazine. pp.56-59

68 - Tuckman, A. (2020) *ADHD After Dark: Better*

Sex Life, Better Relationship. Chapter 2: How ADHD impacts sex and relationships. New York: Routledge. p.35

69 - Tuckman, A. (2020) *ADHD After Dark: Better Sex Life, Better Relationship.* Chapter 2: How ADHD impacts sex and relationships: Porn use frequency. 2020. New York: Routledge. p.40

70 - Lust Cinema (https://lustcinema.com/about)

71 - Jangmo, A. et al (2021) *Attention-Deficit/ Hyperactivity Disorder and Occupational Outcomes: The Role of Educational Attainment, Co-morbid Developmental Disorders, and Intellectual Disability.* PLoS One. (https://www.ncbi.nlm.nih.gov/pmc/ articles/PMC7968636/)

72 - Rodgers, A.L. (2022) *Music Therapy: Sound Medicine for ADHD.* ADDitude magazine. (https:// www.additudemag.com/music-therapy-for-adhd- how-rhythm-builds-focus/#:~:text=Music%20 therapy%20is%20used%20to,hyperactivity%2C%20 and%20strengthens%20social%20skills.)

73 - Varina, R. and Ed. (2021) *28 Masturbation Tips That'll Maximize Your Pleasure.* Updated 22.6.22. (https://www.cosmopolitan.com/sex-love/advice/ a1602/solo-sex/)

74 - Solden, S. and Frank, M. (2019) *A Radical Guide for Women with ADHD: Embrace Neurodiversity and Live Boldly and Break Through Barriers.* Chapter 3: Absorbed Messages. Oakland: New Harbinger Publications. p.41

75 - Gordon, B. (2016) *Mad Girl: A Happy Life with*

a Mixed-up Mind. Chapter 11: I Think I Might Need Some Help. London: Headline Publishing Group. p.290

Chapter Eight: And Then, There It Was

76 - Metz, M.E. et al (2017) *Cognitive-Behavioral Therapy for Sexual Dysfunction.* New York: Routledge.

77 - Holmes, L.A. (2019) *Don't Hold My Head Down: In Search of Some Brilliant Fucking.* Unbound. p.5

78 - Colombo, C. (2022) *What is Rejection Sensitive Dysphoria? The Impact of this Overlooked ADHD Symptom?* The Metro online.

80 - Lovinger, D.M. (1997) *Serotonin's Role in Alcohol's Effects on the Brain.* Alcohol Health Res World. (https://www.ncbi.nlm.nih.gov/pmc/articles/PMC6826824/#:~:text=Serotonin's%20actions%20have%20been%20linked,serotonin%20levels%20compared%20with%20nonalcoholics)

81 - James, L. (2018) *Odd Girl Out: An Autistic Woman in a Neurotypical World.* Colorado: Bluebird. Colorado. pp.194-5

82/83/84 - Solden, S. and Frank, M. (2019) *A Radical Guide for Women with ADHD: Embrace Neurodiversity and Live Boldly and Break Through Barriers.* Oakland: New Harbinger Publications. Chapter 3. p.14

Printed in Great Britain
by Amazon

47098300R00136